Viruses and Molecular Biology

Dean Fraser

Indiana University

The Macmillan Company, New York
Collier-Macmillan Limited, London

This book is dedicated to Max Delbrück, whose pioneering work, critical approach, and evangelical fervor directly or indirectly inspired most of modern phage research.

First Printing

Library of Congress catalog card number: 67–13144

The Macmillan Company, New York

Collier-Macmillan Canada, Ltd., Toronto, Ontario

Printed in the United States of America

Preface

IN THIS BOOK I have tried to dwell on the logical development of virology and on general conclusions. My intent has been to consider viruses as biological objects in their own right, rather than as agents of disease; to discuss the present state of our knowledge of them; and to point out the ways in which the study of viruses has contributed to understanding the fundamentals of biological reproduction and genetics. No real knowledge of chemistry, mathematics, or biology is required of the reader, though obviously a student who has adequate background in these areas will follow certain topics more easily.

I wish to thank Martha Barnes Baylor, who was one of the early converts and who first acquainted me with the bacteriophages. Her enthusiasm has been responsible not only for my indoctrination but also for that of at least two of the major contributors to the area. Wendell M. Stanley offered me the opportunity to begin phage research in his laboratory in Berkeley and to continue there for some seven years. Max Delbrück not only allowed me to work in his laboratory to learn basic phage techniques but has served as a constant model of the sort of critical approach to fundamental problems that has been the hallmark of so much of the phage research since his resurrection of the field.

Priscilla Brooks has patiently typed and retyped the manuscript. The drawings were made by Peter Loewer, whose artistic assistance is appreciated. My students in virology have helped in the clarification of the text, as have the graduate students in my own laboratory. I also wish to thank Angus Graham, who read the manuscript and made valuable suggestions. Finally, I cannot express adequately my appreciation for the help of my wife, Rosemary, who has made nearly painless the application of my nose to the grindstone during the writing of the book, who has disentangled and redacted dozens of sentences, and who has suffered through countless hours of reading the various drafts.

D. F.

Contents

Introduction to the Viruses

What Are Viruses?

THE AVERAGE PERSON thinks of viruses only as agents of disease. When the word "virus" is mentioned he thinks of the common cold, perhaps, or polio or influenza. The average person also knows that when he goes to the doctor with symptoms that are diagnosed as typical of a *viral* infection, the doctor can do little for him except to make him more comfortable and to hasten his recovery by symptomatic treatment. Many formerly common and dreaded *bacterial* diseases, such as pneumonia or scarlet fever, are today seldom heard of, as the result of the development of antibiotics and chemotherapeutic agents. Several other bacterial diseases—notably diphtheria, tetanus, and whooping cough— are under excellent control as the result of the development of vaccines. For several viral diseases of man we also have excellent vaccines, the most successful being those against smallpox, yellow fever, polio, and measles. But in general, the treatment of viral diseases has lagged behind that of bacterial diseases because we have not understood the nature of viruses and their mode of reproduction. Consequently, only the following chapter is devoted to the problems of disease; the subject will be considered mostly from the point of view of the relation of disease to the properties of viruses, rather than the reverse.

It early became apparent that in many ways viruses could be thought of as living. They have inherited properties, such as host and symptom specificity (Figure 1·1)—the virus of measles does not suddenly attack earthworms nor cause mumps—and they reproduce, as we shall see. But the simpler viruses can be considered chemical molecules with clearly defined chemical and physical properties. Scientists from many fields became intrigued with these living macromolecules and their properties; physicists, chemists, mathematicians, biochemists, and others plunged into the study of viruses which burgeoned and ramified at an amazing rate. In the long run, it is almost certainly true that viruses are important mainly as model systems for the understanding of

[A]   [B]   [C]

Figure 1·1. Tobacco mosaic virus symptoms. A: Healthy tobacco plant. **B:** Tobacco plant infected with ordinary TMV. **C:** Tobacco plant infected with a variant of TMV. [Photos supplied by Dr. G. Melchers, Max-Planck Institut für Biologie, Tübingen, Germany. From E. Bünning, *Entwicklungs und Bewegungsphysiologie der Pflanze.* 3. Aufl. *Lehrbuch der Pflanzenphysiologie,* Bd. 2 und 3. Berlin-Göttingen-Heidelberg: Springer 1953.]

problems common to all living things. This will be our primary thesis, and the bacterial parasite T2 will be our primary subject.

The Discovery of Viruses

THE MOSAIC DISEASE OF TOBACCO. Most people believe that viruses were discovered twenty or so years ago. The advances in the conquest of bacterial disease made the public suddenly aware of the viral diseases, which were untouched by the new drugs. In actuality, however, the initial observation on viruses was published in 1894. This was in the classical golden period of bacteriology. The discoveries of Pasteur and Koch and others had established that many diseases of humans, other animals, and plants were caused by bacteria. Certainly many medical men and scientists were convinced that the conquest of all disease was in their grasp—one had only to show that a disease was infectious, isolate and identify the bacterial agent, study its mode of transmission or prepare a vaccine, and the whole problem would be solved.

A quite destructive disease of tobacco, then rampant in Holland, was studied by the Dutch scientist Adolph Mayer in 1885. His observations are important because they illustrate the difference between illness due to heredity, accident, or poor nutrition and that caused by an infectious agent. In studying this striking disease of tobacco plants, which caused a mottling of the leaves in a pattern that he described as "mosaic-like" (Figure 1·1), Mayer showed that a tiny amount of sap from an infected plant could be applied to a healthy one and elicit characteristic damage. This infection would then spread throughout the plant; thus he concluded that the disease was contagious, or transmissible. The demonstration that a disease is indefinitely transmissible constitutes proof that a multiplying agent must be responsible. It is obvious that ordinary small amounts of any poison, for example, would be diluted quickly to nontoxic levels by the physiological fluids of the host organism. Manifestly one cannot transmit poor nutrition in this way nor, in general, hereditary defects. Despite the fact that he was unable, after many attempts, to isolate a bacterium, Mayer assumed that the mosaic disease was of bacterial origin.

A Russian, Ivanovsky, was responsible for the next step and is often cited as the discoverer of viruses. Continuing the study of tobacco mosaic disease, Ivanovsky performed, among others, a standard experiment to show the presence of infective bacteria. This consisted of the demonstration that an infected fluid could be made noninfectious by passing it through an unglazed porcelain filter, the pores of the filter being so fine that bacteria were retained. But to his surprise, filtration failed to remove the infectious agent from the juice of infected plants. In addition Ivanovsky was unable to isolate any bacteria. Nonetheless, like most of us, he was blinded by his prejudices and assumed that the agent was bacterial in nature. He did no further experiments and his results were neglected for several years.

Mayer's experiments were also repeated and extended, apparently without knowledge of Ivanovsky's work, by the great Dutch bacteriologist Beijerinck, who published his results in 1898. Unlike his predecessors, however, Beijerinck immediately recognized the importance of the transmission of the disease by a filtrate and stated that a new infectious principle was involved—a "contagium vivum fluidum" (infectious living fluid). He reported elaborately on his fruitless attempts to visualize bacteria in extracts of the plants, on his ability to transmit the disease indefinitely with a filtrate, on the fact that the filtrate on standing seemed neither to gain nor to lose ability to transmit the disease, and on the fact that the infectious agent could diffuse through agar, another characteristic not possessed by bacteria. He also speculated that several other plant diseases—specifically peach yellows and peach rosette— might be similar in being caused by an infectious fluid.

VIRAL DISEASES OF ANIMALS. In the same year, 1898, the German bacteriologists Loeffler and Frosch demonstrated that foot-and-mouth disease of cattle is similarly caused by a filtrate apparently free of any bacteria but able to spread the disease, as they calculated and demonstrated, far beyond any believable dilution of a toxin or poison. In a remarkably perceptive paper they speculated that perhaps many other diseases might also be caused by these new, very small reproducing and infectious agents. They specifically mentioned smallpox, cowpox, typhus, and cattle plague. Noting the size of the smallest known bacteria to be some 0.5 to 1.0 micron diameter, they suggested that the agent of foot-and-mouth disease, if particulate, must be perhaps one-fifth to one-tenth this diameter. They pointed out that such particles would be invisible in the light microscope and would pass through filters that held bacteria. Their guess that viruses might be some 50–100 millimicrons in diameter was strikingly close to the truth, and constituted an improvement over Beijerinck's notion that the viruses were a true fluid.

The actual term *virus* was applied by Beijerinck to describe the agent of tobacco mosaic disease (now called tobacco mosaic virus or, simply and more usually, TMV), but at that time *virus* was a general term for any specific morbid principle, anything from a true toxin to bacteria. Hence the new small agents came to be called *filterable viruses* to distinguish them from the larger bacteria. This expression was in common use for several decades, but as the term *virus* in its general sense gradually disappeared and came to be applied only to the filterable agents, eventually the *filterable* qualification was dropped.

The Demonstration of Viruses as Agents of Disease

As time went on, many already known diseases—mumps, chicken pox, hog cholera—as well as many newly identified diseases, were found to be caused by these filterable agents.

Among the animals, viruses were found to attack many vertebrates, including fish (carp pox) and amphibians (the virus-induced kidney tumor of the leopard frog). A new group of viruses was discovered with the study of silkworm diseases, responsible in France and Japan for considerable economic loss in the silk industry, which has since virtually succumbed to the nonfilterable organic chemist who made nylon. Dozens of new plant viruses were discovered. Several criteria are commonly used for classifying a disease as viral: (1) The gross symptoms, in animal or plant, often indicate to the trained observer almost certain viral causation. Microscopically observable pathological symptoms are also important. A frequent concomitant of viral infection is the presence of microscopically visible *inclusion bodies* in the cells of the infected host. A fairly new technique involves the use of fluorescent antibody as a specific stain for a suspected virus in cells of a tissue section. (2) The disease is *not* susceptible to antibiotics of the types known to be effective against bacteria. (3) No bacterial, fungal, or other cellular agent can be demonstrated by microscopic examination or by standard laboratory cultural techniques. (4) The fluid responsible for transmission can be passed without loss of infectivity through filters capable of retaining bacteria. (5) In suitable tissue or cell culture the filterable agent reproduces and causes observable cytopathogenic effects.

The first of these criteria obviously is only a practical one for primary diagnosis. The second is often considered as confirmatory but is loosely used and, as with all negative criteria, is not really definitive. All too often the clinical doctor notes symptoms which might be typical of a viral infection and, finding that one or two of the wide spectrum antibiotics have no effect, dismisses the patient with the statement that he undoubtedly has a viral disease and that the best thing is to go to bed with a good book and take aspirin. In most instances he is right, but sometimes he is not. The third criterion is also negative. The fourth is a much safer one, though seldom used in clinical or field work. We now recognize that there exists a considerable spectrum of transmissible agents, ranging from the small bacteria through the pleuropneumonia- and psitticosis-types of agents, the large complicated viruses—for example, vaccinia—and the simpler viruses, which cover a range of average size nearly of an order of magnitude (that is to say a factor of tenfold). This point is illustrated in Figure 1·2. It will be noticed that the minute objects range from highly organized, cellular structures to viruses that are smaller than the largest protein molecules. The fifth criterion is now very widely used. Many animal and human viruses have been demonstrated to cause cytopathogenic effects (Figure 1·3), and experiments to this end constitute the first step toward any serious study of an animal virus.

The Discovery of Bacterial Viruses

The English scientist F. W. Twort first suggested that a virus existed that was capable of attacking bacteria. His report of "degenerative changes" in colonies of various bacteria, published in 1915 in the journal *Lancet,* went virtually unnoticed; and Twort himself did little additional work because of his involvement in the first World War. In 1917, however, a Canadian, F. d'Herelle, discovered that the intestinal contents of normal individuals or convalescent patients yielded a filter-able principle which he called "bacteriophage" *—that is, "eater of bacteria," because of its property of dissolving or, as we now say, *lysing* bacterial cells of intestinal origin. These reports published in various French journals attracted great attention in medical circles and led to an enormous amount of work devoted to attempts to use bacteriophages therapeutically to cure bacterial infections. Though it is still not en-tirely clear why this work was so unsuccessful, the failure is probably explained by several facts: (1) Bacteriophages are very specific. It is necessary to find a different one for virtually every infection. (2) We now know that many bacteria have the ability to mutate at a rapid rate to become resistant to the bacteriophages. (3) It is apparently also true that animals possess nonspecific virus-resisting humoral (circulating) factors which probably kill the virus faster than it can destroy the bacterial cells.

Soon d'Herelle came to believe that bacteriophages were viruses that attack bacteria, but a number of people working in the area disputed this vigorously. The fact became generally accepted in the 1930's.

---

* This word is pronounced in two ways: to rhyme either with *age* or with *garage;* similarly the shorter form *phage* is pronounced in both ways with nearly equal frequency. The plural, *bacteriophages,* is ordinarily applied only when more than one group is involved, as "T1 and T7 bacteriophages."

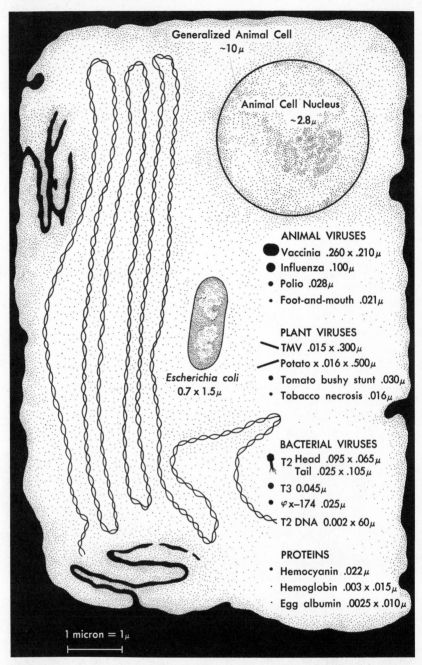

Figure 1·2. Representation of an animal cell, a bacterial cell, and various viruses and proteins. The drawing is to scale, except for the width of the T2DNA, which is greatly enlarged. (The thickness of a page in this book is approximately 100 microns.)

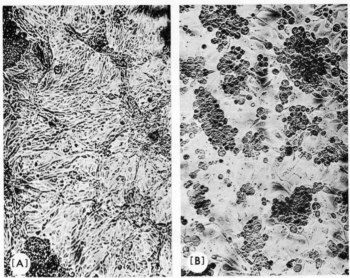

Figure 1·3. Cytopathic effect of adenovinus in human kidney cell culture (×225). **A:** Uninfected. **B:** Infected. [From G. D. Hsiung, *Diagnostic Virology*, New Haven, Conn.: Yale University Press, 1964, p. 85.]

The Beginnings of the Modern Period of Viral Research

In the period 1930–1940 a new era in biochemistry and biology began, largely in America, with the study of enzymes, the specific catalysts that carry out virtually all of the chemical reactions of living organisms. The purification of enzymes culminated in the work of James Sumner and John Northrop, who succeeded in actually crystallizing various enzymes. It was considered axiomatic that one could not crystallize a "life force" but that one could crystallize chemical compounds. The real significance of this work was to drive another nail in the coffin of vitalism—a central "mystery of life" was now explainable in chemical and physical terms.

Wendell M. Stanley, an organic chemist, felt that perhaps viruses, too, were large proteins capable of self-reproduction in a suitable host cell. Working in a relatively uncharted area, Stanley undertook the tedious process of the purification and chemical study of a virus using again TMV. It was no coincidence that this first discovered of the viruses was chosen; it was known that TMV occurred in infected plants in huge amounts, and the plants could be grown in virtually unlimited quantity, if it became necessary, and at a reasonable cost. The virus had physical properties that made it easy to differentiate from cell components. These facts would seldom be true of any animal virus, and the bacteriophages were, at that time, not even surely identified as viruses. After many months of work, Stanley's efforts were crowned with an almost unbelievable success. He was able to concentrate the TMV to such a high purity that it crystallized, and his first analysis showed that it, like the enzymes, indeed seemed to be a protein. Actually it was soon found that the pure virus contains phosphorus and is, therefore, not a protein but a *nucleoprotein*. Proteins, of course, are huge molecules built up of amino acids. Nucleic acids, however, are unusual among natural organic molecules in that they contain phosphorus. We shall consider the structure and properties of nucleic acids in some detail in later chapters.

Viruses as Living Molecules

The discovery that viruses could be crystallized (Figure 1·4) like a chemical molecule and yet retain their ability to cause disease (and to multiply as though alive) led to a great controversy. Are they living or dead? As with many controversies in science this one was not so much

Figure 1·4. Crystals of tomato bushy stunt virus (×225). [Photo supplied by Dr. F. C. Bawden, Rothamsted Experimental Station, Harpenden, England.]

settled as relegated to a position of unimportance. In general it may be said that the answer depends on the definition of *life*. If one insists that life involves the acquisition and conversion of food or the response to stimuli, then viruses are certainly not alive unless one considerably strains the meaning of these terms. But in the sense that viruses have genetic properties and can mutate, and in the sense that they can reproduce, albeit completely parasitically, they certainly are alive. The important thing is that these last two properties are the sine qua non of *all* living things. Viruses are the smallest and simplest objects showing these two properties, and they have few if any other properties to confuse their study. That is to say, they are a model system for the study of reproduction and genetics: physically, chemically, and biologically.

Stanley's discovery had the effect of dramatizing these properties of viruses as being on the borderline between life and nonlife; he was awarded the Nobel Prize, in conjunction with Sumner and Northrop, in 1946. Others quickly showed that numerous viruses could be purified and crystallized, and the study of viruses by chemists and physicists as well as biologists soon constituted an important part of the new field of molecular biology. The idea that all properties of living organisms must, in the final analysis, depend upon and be explainable in terms of chemical and physical properties of molecules and their interactions is still offensive to some, but few modern biologists doubt it.

The Taxonomy and Nomenclature of Viruses

Ordinarily in science, especially in biology, one of the first steps in any new area is that of classification and the development of a systematic nomenclature for the objects or phenomena under study. In biology it is traditional to approach the teaching by this neat if somewhat arbitrary avenue. With viruses, however, we find that diverse studies have progressed to an amazing degree with no satisfactory special taxonomy. Ordinarily one classifies with respect to size, morphology (both macroscopic and microscopic), function, physical properties, environmental associations, and so on. But with the viruses the naming has come about more haphazardly than one might believe possible. Most are simply named by the disease they cause. Many human diseases, and hence their viruses, have traditional or trivial names such as mumps, smallpox, influenza, and rabies. Sheep blue tongue and foot-and-mouth disease are typical of most animal viral diseases in that they are named in terms of their hosts or outstanding symptoms, as are most plant viral diseases —for example, tobacco mosaic virus, sugar beet curly top, peach rosette, maize streak, turnip yellow mosaic, aster yellows, cranberry false blossom, potato witch's broom, and cacao swollen shoot. Rous sarcoma, like many tumor diseases, is named for its discoverer and the type of tumor. Fiji disease, Murray Valley fever, Semliki Forest fever, Coxsackie, and Sendai are examples of many diseases and viruses named in terms of locale of occurrence or discovery. Some are romantically strange and wonderful: ndumu, quaranfil, o'nyong-nyong, bussuquara, spondweni, zika, ieri, eg ar 1306, and—my special favorite—snotsiecke, a disease of the gnu. Bacterial viruses are given short, utilitarian, unromantic names such as T2 or P22. An attempt to establish a systematic nomenclature and taxonomy (F. O. Holmes) met with almost complete nonacceptance.

We now know enough about viruses to attempt reasonable classification; and with the animal viruses, at least, systematology based on fundamental structure, both chemical and physical, and on biological characteristics is gradually being established. We find the *arboviruses,* a group with many distinguishing properties in common, including the fact that they are all carried by insects (*a*rthropod *b*orne), comprising such members as the many encephalitic viruses, yellow fever, and dengue. The *enteroviruses* include the various strains of polio, Coxsackie viruses, and ECHO (*e*nteric *c*ytopathogenic *h*uman *o*rphan) viruses. These viruses have in common the fact that their main theater of operation is the gut, despite the reputation of polio viruses, at least, as destroyers of nervous tissue. The *herpes viruses* are rather larger and more complicated morphologically than the foregoing and are typified by the virus of the common cold sore and pseudorabies. The *myxoviruses* are distinguished by their affinity for the mucin layer of red blood cells (*myxo-* is a Greek prefix referring to slime) and their ability to agglutinate various types of red cells. Members include influenza, mumps, and parainfluenza viruses of humans, Newcastle of chickens, and a number of related influenza-like viruses of other animals, including Sendai and SV (*s*imian *v*irus) 5. The *pox viruses* include smallpox, vaccinia, and molluscum contagiosum. These viruses are large, brick-shaped, and complicated in morphology. They cause pocks on the chorioallantoic membrane of the embryonated egg and are characterized by the formation of large inclusion bodies in infected cells. The DNA-containing *papovaviruses* (*pa*pilloma, *po*lyoma, *va*cuolating) cause wartlike excrescences on the skin of their various hosts. The *adenoviruses* constitute a very large group responsible for respiratory infections and first characterized by their ability to cause degeneration of adenoid tissue. Probably many "common colds" diagnosed by the victim or family physician are due to adenoviruses. At least one of the viruses of this group can cause cancer in mice, a recently noted and repulsive fact. The *reoviruses* (*r*espiratory, *e*nteric, *o*rphan) are entertaining in that it is not clear that they cause any disease; they have been identified mainly by cytopathogenic effects in tissue culture.

An attempt to begin classifying viruses in terms of fundamental properties has begun. (Naturally, a committee was formed.) As a result we have the *picorna* virus group, a monument to scientific cuteness. *Pico* is a prefix implying very small size (a picogram = 10^{-12}g); these are very small viruses 15–30mμ in diameter. But *picorna* also reminds us that the group contains *po*lio, *C*oxsackie, *o*rphan and *r*hino viruses (common cold symptoms) and that all members are *i*nsensitive to ether and contain *RNA.* One wonders what the committee will do for an encore.

I note the beginnings of classification of the bacterial viruses, and the monumental task of classifying the hundreds of plant viruses will eventually come about as they are studied in sufficient detail. Perhaps all of this emphasizes that even science can sometimes progress in an unsystematic way. When the excitement of discovery in a new area leaves too little time for slow, painstaking classification and step-by-step progress, many unanswered questions and problems may be left temporarily by the wayside.

Summary

Discovered in the 1890's, viruses are very small, virtually ubiquitous parasites of living cellular organisms. Although they are agents of a multitude of diseases, and share with other living organisms genetic functions and the ability to reproduce, it is possible to describe them in terms of the properties of chemical molecules.

2

Viruses as Agents of Disease

VIRUSES ARE KNOWN to attack a tremendous variety of living forms all the way from single-celled organisms, both plant and animal, to large trees and mammals. Although there are important groups (for example gymnosperms) for which none are *known,* viruses have usually been found when serious attempts were made to find them. It is not impossible to think that they are virtually ubiquitous parasites of all cellular organisms.

Mild Viruses

To categorize viruses as parasites as is usually done may be a calumny. Certainly it is true that many, if not most, viruses multiply harmlessly, or nearly so, in their natural hosts. Studies at the National Institutes of Health have shown that a group of human volunteers had a constant succession of viruses, demonstrable as showing damaging (cytopathogenic) effects to tissue cultures but causing little or no discomfort to the human host. The deadly (to humans) encephalitic viruses seem to live naturally and harmlessly in fowl. Viruses causing the "flaming" or "breaking" (striking patterns of color on the petals) of tulips and the striping of the leaves of the common house plant Abutilon appear to cause little or no damage to the plant. The same is true of a number of viruses known to multiply in insect vectors seemingly without damage. Some involve plants as the injured host (aster yellows and clover club leaf viruses) or animals (the encephalitic viruses). Since such instances have been found more or less incidentally, one may suspect that there are many more; in fact the nonpathogenic relationship may be the usual case. From an evolutionary viewpoint the mild or harmless virus is the most successful one in that it does not bite the hand that feeds it. The extreme instance of the mild virus is the masked virus, which will be discussed in the last chapter.

We may consider viruses in some ways as beneficial. As we shall see in the final chapter, it is clear that viruses may serve as agents for genetic recombination, at least among the bacteria. This is a property of considerable potential survival value to these organisms. It has been suggested that viruses may serve as a biological warfare agent—to enable a microorganism to control competitors in its vicinity—but I know of no evidence for this. We have used several insect viruses to control insect pests, and myxomatosis helped reduce the rabbit population of Australia. Also, it is indisputable that viruses are providing a good living and an unbelievably fascinating research area for hundreds of scientists. Nothing is all bad in this best of all possible worlds.

Public Health and Epidemiology

To return to the subject of diseases of humans, other animals, and plants, it is obvious that here our primary object has been to try to find out how the viruses cause disease, in each instance, and how to prevent them from doing so. It is true even today, however, that we have little success in controlling viral disease in the individual. Antibiotics so far developed are useful only against bacteria and fungi, not viruses, though there are glimmerings of success in this area. We have, therefore, devoted our efforts largely to *preventing* the individual from getting the disease through personal hygiene and immunization and to *preventing* spread in a population, through application of principles learned in the generalized study of public health and epidemiology.

The history of epidemiology is a fascinating subject filling many books. We shall consider here only the principles involved. Once it had been realized that diseases spread from the sick to the healthy, the main foundation of epidemiology had been laid. Obviously it remained only to discover *how* this was accomplished and then to prevent it. Oddly, with many of the best known viral diseases this is still by no means established.

The most fundamental principle of epidemiology is *quarantine*. Isolate the infected individual and he will not spread the disease. Formal legal quarantine seems to have disappeared. The principle, however, is as sound as ever, and the friend who comes to your party sneezing vigorously and cheerfully telling everyone that he has a cold may be socially acceptable, for reasons not clear, but he is public-health-wise unsound and probably doing his friends no favor. It is an article of faith that the respiratory viruses are spread by sneezing and coughing, though the evidence is poor at best and scarcely extends beyond folk observation and belief. Laboratory demonstrations have proved astonishingly difficult.

Some viruses (for example, smallpox) are believed to spread directly on objects (so-called *fomites*), handled by one person and passed to another, others (as polio) through a fecal-oral cycle mediated literally by hand to mouth or by feces to water to mouth (for example, ugh, in swimming pools). There is, again, little hard evidence for these beliefs.

Obviously the principle of quarantine is based on them, however, and it is generally effective.

Public health measures of all sorts are the second most important principle. The protection of water supplies from contamination and the purification of the water by filtration and chlorination are clearly of great importance with such diseases as infectious hepatitis. Similarly the sanitary processing of sewage is a keystone in epidemiology. The insistence on proper standards of sanitation in all places open to the public is important particularly where food is served. These measures, however, although of unquestionable value in viral epidemiology, have been demonstrated most clearly with bacterial diseases.

Vectors and Reservoirs

Most viruses are highly specific. Poliomyelitis, for example, is probably a natural disease only in humans and certain primates. The common cold seems restricted to humans, and so on. There are notable exceptions. Rabies seems to be capable of infecting and killing most, if not all, warm-blooded animals, and it is curiously so that many viruses alternate between two or more specific hosts with amazing disregard for taxonomic relationships. In the control of viral diseases the greatest clear successes have come by recognition of these facts through discovery of the vector and the reservoir. For example, mosquitoes are responsible for the transmission of (are *vectors* for) yellow fever. Suggested by Carlos Finlay and demonstrated by a group of doctors under Walter Reed, this fact was the key to modern epidemiology and to the successful digging of the Panama Canal, not to mention the exploitation of Africa by the white race. It is now known that many diseases, most notably the encephalitic fevers which periodically ravage the human population of the major river valleys of the temperate and tropical world, are mosquito spread. A fascinating discovery was that each such disease has its own species, or small group of species, of mosquitoes, and that control can be accomplished nowadays usually quite quickly by attacking the chain of transmission through extermination of the mosquito vector in its known habitat.

The *reservoir* is a host in which the virus exists in a mild form. Most virologists feel that this is the usual way for a virus to live; with the encephalitic viruses, again, it has been shown that fowl are the natural hosts. It is believed that the transmission of encephalitis from fowl to fowl by mosquitoes is the normal cycle and that the escape of the virus with deadly effect into man or horses (with eastern and western equine encephalitis, for example) is an odd occurrence traceable to an unusually high level of infected fowl and an unusually high level of mosquitoes. It is also well known that many human viruses normally cause mild intestinal disease. A few members of this group of *entero*viruses very occasionally (perhaps a few per 100,000 infected) also attack nervous tissue with serious to fatal results. The most notable example is polio, which most people think of as a disease only of nervous tissue. In this instance the subclinically infected human is very common and might be considered the reservoir for the serious disease.

Immunization

It is something of a fad today to consider public health, personal hygiene, and general epidemiology pretty dull subjects, fit for study and practice by dull people, despite the obvious fact that most of our advances against disease are clearly to be attributed to them. Much more glamorous is vaccination (immunization). This is, of course, protection of the individual and only by extension to the population an epidemiological measure. But an aura of mystery and magic surrounds it—protecting one against a disease by sticking him with a little needle containing a bit of milky fluid. Viral diseases are among those most successfully controlled by immunization, yet when one has named smallpox, yellow fever, polio, measles, and rabies he has a pretty complete list. In my opinion the less said about influenza vaccination the better; the effectiveness is far from complete and is short-lived, and in many people the result is a good imitation of the disease.

The principle of immunization can be stated fairly simply, although the details are beyond our scope. With most infectious diseases the recovered patient is specifically resistant for a time varying from a few months (influenza) to life (measles). This is due to the production, in the tissues of warm-blooded animals, of proteins called *antibodies* which have a structural configuration specifically related to that of some component of or from the infectious agent. This component is a large molecule, a protein or polysaccharide or complex of substances such as lipoproteins or lipopolysaccharides. These are called *antigens*. The fundamental principle of specific induced immunity is that if the antigen characteristic of the disease organism can be made harmless to the human or animal and yet retain its ability to form antibody, it can be used to immunize. Vaccine, the antigen, in the case of viruses is usually the whole virus itself, and it is made harmless in one of two general ways: (1) either the virus is killed, as with formaldehyde in the Salk vaccine against polio, or (2) it is cultivated in some alternate host until it has lost its pathogenicity (become *attenuated*) for the human. The attenuation is not as the term seems to imply, a weakening of the individual virus, but occurs by a process of mutation and selection in this alternate host. When it is successful the mutant strain so selected can grow in the original host and retain its ability to act as an antigen capable of inducing antibody against the original pathogenic strain, but the disease produced is either nil or unimportant. Examples of this are smallpox vaccine, where the altered virus was originally the naturally occurring cowpox virus and is now a laboratory strain (vaccinia) or the live virus vaccine for polio, where the altered strains were selected by extensive cultivation and testing in other animals. This principle, understood from the time of Pasteur, was employed recently in an important way in the work of the American virologist Albert Sabin. However produced, the antibody reacts with the virus antigen(s) and prevents the virus from attacking the cells of the host.

The reasons why we have so few vaccines are many. Among them are the following: (1) lack of good naturally occurring immunity—influenza; (2) the occurrence of so many strains of the virus—the common cold—that it is unfeasible to protect against all of them; (3) comparative rareness of the disease, making impractical the immunization of the whole population—rabies (our most successful vaccine, smallpox, probably causes more deaths per annum than rabies in the United States); (4) mildness of the disease—chicken pox; (5) complexity of vaccine testing and production in these days of great solicitude for the individual (if Edward Jenner today tried his experiments on humans which in the late eighteenth century led to smallpox vaccination, he would be unfrocked and driven out of the medical profession); (6) public apathy, fear, and chintziness. Unless compelled through legislation (smallpox), most people are unwilling to subject themselves or even their pets (rabies vaccination in dogs) to immunization even when it is free, except in the face of an epidemic, when it may be too late.

Personal Hygiene

Toilet paper in governmental buildings in Britain has printed on each sheet, "Now wash your hands." We are told from birth to wash before meals, avoid diseased people, refrain from the use of communal dishes and cups, restrict our lovemaking to the suitably hygienic, and so on. There is so little doubt of the value of this that I wish to be the devil's advocate. Personal hygiene is even more passé, in some circles, than public health. The "in" group now makes a fetish of untidiness. They have a point. Several years ago I had a frenzied phone call from a mother who said that she had been referred to me as an expert and that her child was chronically ill. She boiled all its toys, she sterilized all its food, she exercised extreme care to avoid infected companions, but it had one ailment after another. My personal suspicion was that she could have done no worse, but I referred her to her friendly M.D. and said that I was no expert. If anything is clear it is that we are immune to some diseases because we are exposed to them from birth. Measles is a classic example. Among primitive and isolated people the mortality from measles can run to 30 per cent; we in the United States, however, receive maternal antibody and are then exposed virtually from birth, with the result that the disease is nearly always mild (though actually even in the United States it is more fatal than polio). Clearly we have minimized many bacterial diseases (for example, typhoid fever) and certainly some viral diseases (for example, polio) mostly by public health and personal hygiene, but equally clearly the presence of antibody or of the potential for booster response is our chief weapon against much disease. As public health standards and personal hygiene improve, we must be increasingly prepared to substitute artificial immunization for the natural immunity now acquired by continual or sporadic exposure. We are still far from knowing all the answers, and we should remember that the human race has existed for hundreds of millenia because of natural immune mechanisms. Without deprecating hygiene, immunization, or public health, the natural human tendency toward the principle of limited sloppiness is probably sound, as we zigzag toward the conquest of disease.

Interferons

It has long been known that humans and other animals have, in their armamentarium of defense mechanisms, seemingly innate, rather nonspecific antiviral factors (for example, *properdin*). In the past few years, however, another discovery has been made. Cells of animals, plants, and bacteria infected with one virus frequently become immune to other viruses. It has been shown that in animals this is due to the production in the infected cells of substances called interferons which may have a wide spectrum of antiviral activities. So far interferon does not seem useful against the more dangerous viruses, but there is great interest in utilizing the phenomenon to protect against such viruses as cause the common cold, because there are so many strains that there is as yet little hope for control with vaccines. Induced production of interferon protects experimental animals and does not even require a viral infection; foreign nucleic acids or certain polysaccharides seem to work. Some occur seemingly naturally. It will be interesting to follow this area which is being feverishly investigated by several pharmaceutical firms.

Epidemiological Cycles

A well-known feature of a number of viral diseases is that they tend to run in cycles. Some cycles are annual. Diseases such as influenza and the common cold seem strongly seasonal, perhaps because of the effect of low humidity in heated rooms on the stability of the virus in aerosols (as demonstrated with measles) and/or an increased susceptibility of semidry upper respiratory tissues. With the encephalitic viruses the annual cycle is clearly tied to seasonal variations in the population of the mosquito vector. Other viral diseases occur most frequently in longer cycles; influenza A seems to occur fairly regularly at two- or three-year intervals. Although the reasons for this are no doubt very complex, in principle the main parameters seem clear. If a disease has a high infection rate it may sweep through a population quite rapidly. Infected individuals shed virus which is transmitted to others. But the eventual result is a population rendered largely immune—that is to say, with a high level of antibodies against this virus. The virus then dies out through lack of susceptible hosts, and the epidemic is ended. Eventually, however, previously unexposed children grow up, previously exposed adults lose antibodies—a natural process occurring over months or even years—until they no longer have adequate levels, and the population now has enough susceptible members to sustain another epidemic. Some viruses with extreme infectivity and mortality can actually put themselves out of business. Fowl plague, for example, sweeps through a flock with extreme speed, but there are so few survivors that further spread is relatively easy to control. Other viruses, with low infectivity, may keep going at a reasonably steady rate, since there is always a sufficient pool of susceptibles to permit further infections. An example of this might be rabies which, although 100 per cent fatal, spreads so inefficiently and has such a long incubation time that its incidence remains rather steady from year to year. Measles and mumps, also, seem to depend on a constantly renewed supply of fresh children but keep going at a steady rate in an annual cycle. Very elaborate mathematical models of epidemiology have been created based on the assumptions and facts here sketched.

Viruses and Cancer

It would not be reasonable to abandon the discussion of viruses and human disease without considering explicitly the possible role of viruses in human cancer. This is a topic fraught with current controversy. There is no question whatsoever that many animal cancers (Rous sarcoma, mouse leukemia, mouse mammary tumor, and others) are caused by viruses. There is little question that many human cancers are closely parallel to some of the proved examples of viral causation in animal tumors. We know that the Bittner mouse mammary tumor virus is transmitted through the mother's milk. The Rous sarcoma agent is a defective virus which can multiply only with the help of a relative. We know that temperate viruses of bacteria are transmitted for many generations as part of the bacterial chromosome and only stimulated to reproduction by certain kinds of carcinogenic (cancer-causing) agents. But because of the difficulties of unbiased human observation and the impossibility of human experimentation with this uncontrollable type of disease, little evidence has been obtained as to how many of these factors (if any) apply to humans and human cancer. In a number of human cancers the electron microscope reveals "inclusions" suggestive of viruses. A number of studies seem to show evidence of foci of "infection" with leukemias in certain schools or houses or locations. A long-term study of a sarcoma of the jaw in Africa seems to indicate clearly the spread of a human cancer by some insect vector. Thus cancer *may* occur through infection or by arousal of a masked, possibly parentally transmitted virus. But whether *any* human cancers are *actually* so caused is a question not yet surely answered. The problem is clearly complex. Heredity appears to be important, and so also are carcinogenic factors such as cigarettes, mother's milk, and coal tar (if you happen to be a chimney sweep). Perhaps diet is significant too (if you happen to exist on charcoal-broiled steaks or coffee), and possibly religion (few nuns develop cancer of the cervix, but the incidence of cancer of the uterus is unusually high). The best practical advice seems to be to enjoy life while keeping an eye on the literature without taking it too seriously until confirmed.

Animal Viruses

I have devoted most of the space to human viruses on the principle that college students from the cities and suburbs are superbly anthropocentric and could not care less about animal and plant viruses. Actually I am shortchanging you thereby. Many of the topics previously discussed could be considered in some instances more profitably by using animal or plant viruses as examples. All domestic animals are plagued by one or more important viruses. One could name distemper in dogs, gastroenteritis in cats, hog cholera, foot-and-mouth disease in cattle, fowl plague, carp pox in goldfish, and snotsiecke in the gnu, just to give a round sample. The principles discussed above are applicable to animal viral epidemics. One can quarantine, employ sanitation with respect to food and wastes, and immunize as with humans. Since one can far more easily experiment with new vaccines on animals than on the alleged (by us) pinnacle of creation, the human, it is no surprise that there are many quite successful vaccines for domestic animals—for example, rabies, distemper, hepatitis in dogs, and hog cholera. For others the same difficulties crop up as discussed for the human viruses. There seem to be far too many strains of foot-and-mouth disease, for example, to allow a vaccine for this devastating ailment of cattle. A new principle now appears in that one can, in an emergency, control the spread of an epidemic by slaughter of all infected herds. This was done wholesale in an outbreak of foot-and-mouth disease in Mexico a few years ago and was, if only at enormous expense, successful in eliminating the threat to the United States cattle industry. A possible new principle is the selection or breeding of virus-resistant animals. In actuality I do not know of an instance of this having been done deliberately, although some breeds are more virus-resistant than others. It seems more practical to breed animals for other qualities and to protect them from disease by sanitation, quarantine, slaughter of infected herds, and vaccination.

Plant Viruses

The viral diseases of plants are legion. There are said to be over fifty viruses attacking the Elberta peach alone. Many plant viruses are of enormous economic importance; it is clear that with a number of crops —tobacco, sugar beet, tomatoes, for example—the damage in the United States alone runs into millions of dollars a year. Intensive research has shown that the viruses are spread in a fascinating variety of ways. We cannot possibly do justice to this subject even in a cursory way.

The most common modes of spreading are the following: (1) by sucking insects—leafhopper and aphids with a multitude of viruses (peach yellows), (2) mechanically by agricultural workers and implements (tobacco mosaic), (3) through the seeds of infected plants (various bean viruses, as southern bean mosaic), (4) through tubers (potato viruses) or other vegetative propagation. The methods of control lean heavily on insect spraying and roguing—the destruction by burning and plowing under of infected crops. With the plants, however, the breeding of resistant varieties has been widely practiced, as can readily be seen from perusal of any seed or plant catalogue. Another effective control is the prohibition of transport of plants, fruit, and so on, from areas of epidemic. Confiscation of fruit at the California border has been claimed to be successful in excluding several crop diseases.

Viral and Host Evolution

Consideration of viruses as agents of disease should not fail to take into account the obvious fact that the relationship of these apparent parasites to their hosts and reservoirs illustrates evolutionary processes in a number of clear-cut ways. Viral transmission can be extremely efficient (as with measles) or extremely inefficient (as with rabies), but must in each case result in constantly making susceptible hosts available to the virus. The virus that wipes out its host dooms itself in the process, unless it can adapt to new hosts. Such mutations in viruses are well known with the bacteriophages. An alternative is for the virus to mutate to less virulence. This process has been apparent in the relationship of myxomatosis to the rabbit population of Australia. In this case a virus mild for Brazilian rabbits proved extremely virulent to the Australian strain. After purposeful introduction, it reduced the enormous rabbit population of the continent by over 90 per cent. Through natural evolution and selection the introduced strain has been gradually replaced with less potent mutants. Meanwhile the rabbit population has successfully developed resistant members. Indeed we must assume that such mutations have been universal and that the development of the nonspecific antiviral factors in higher animals and of the antibody mechanism are examples of this constant interplay of selective forces in evolution. As we shall see in later chapters, viruses have acquired a fantastic ability to exist in difficult environments, to utilize the normal metabolic activities of the host for their own multiplication, and to alter the situation just sufficiently to ensure success for the virus at the expense of the host.

Summary

The causation of severe disease is probably an extreme example of the general relationship between a virus and its host. In combating viral disease, we must rely mostly on breaking the cycle of transmission by isolation of the sick or elimination of the agent of transmission. Immunization frequently offers an effective means of protection of humans and domestic animals.

3

The Culture of Viruses

LABORATORY STUDY of a virus must begin with the development of a practical method of culturing it. One can, of course, simply take the natural host into the laboratory. With many viruses this is a reasonable thing to do; with others it is necessary to adapt the virus to a convenient laboratory host. There is little doubt that the best known viruses are those for which one or the other of these alternatives proved relatively easy.

If we are interested in studies of the biological relationship of the virus with a cell, ideally the host cells should be biologically uniform, as in a cell culture. When the host is a whole plant (as with TMV in tobacco) or animal (as with influenza in the mouse) one never knows in which of the myriad types of cells of the complicated organism the processes to be studied are occurring. If we use a cell culture, however, we must realize that with the viral diseases of higher forms this means that we are then studying a model system which may have little relevancy to the natural virus-host relationship. Experience so far, however, suggests that this pessimism is unjustified. In any event, a simple system is clearly the place to begin.

An alternative possible first step in understanding a virus is to study its physical and chemical properties. Studies of this kind impose requirements that are somewhat different from those for the usual kind of biological studies. Since we must be able to prepare relatively large quantities of virus free from extraneous material, the situation is more favorable if the virus has distinctive properties and is reasonably concentrated in the host at the outset. It can be seen historically, in the work of Wendell Stanley on TMV for example, that progress came first when these conditions were met.

Plant Virus Cultivation—TMV

To anyone who has smelled cage rooms full of stinking mice, who has put up with the unreasoning obstreperousness of a flock of hens, who has been bitten by monkeys, or who has contemplated experiments on chimpanzees at some two hundred dollars each, to anyone, in short, who has worked with almost any whole animal, the idea of working with a nice clean, quiet, sunny, greenhouse full of plants has tremendous appeal. Scientists are a determined lot, however, and the choice of tobacco mosaic virus as the first one to be cultivated in style was based on other factors. It is true that tobacco plants are relatively easy to grow quickly and are amenable to greenhouse cultivation. Moreover a quantitative assay (of which more later) was available to Stanley when he undertook the purification of TMV. But the important consideration was that the virus could be cultivated in large quantities at high titers in a reasonable space in a short time. It is possible to infect a group of eight-week-old plants with a small quantity of starting virus and to obtain literally grams of TMV in a matter of a few weeks. There is probably no other virus (with the possible exception of certain insect viruses) that occurs in equivalent quantities and concentrations under natural conditions. For biochemical work, then, this viral system proved in many ways ideal; and, as we shall see, the purification of TMV and the elucidation of its chemical and physical structure and properties proved a major factor in the inauguration of the modern era of viral research.

The methods used for production of TMV are applicable with some modifications to a considerable number of plant viruses. Many host plants can easily be grown and infected and will yield substantial quantities of virus. But there is a great weakness of the plant virus systems which has not been overcome satisfactorily to this day. We cannot readily cultivate plant tissue as individual cells or a clone of cells (that is to say, a group derived from a single cell as parent). Furthermore all plant viruses seem to require introduction into the susceptible cell by either injury of the cell or deposition in some quite specific way, as by an insect vector. These factors have severely limited biological and biochemical studies of virus-host relationships.

Animal Virus Culture in Eggs

With animal viruses the situation at first was even worse than with the plant viruses. When the natural host was the human, and the disease serious, as in the case of polio, study was virtually impossible until it was found that the virus could infect monkeys. And it was only when strains were found that would grow in certain varieties of rats and mice that real progress became possible.

One of the most studied animal viruses has been that of influenza. This is not because of the importance of the ordinarily mild disease. It is rather the old story of the drunk looking for his keys under the street light instead of down the block where he dropped them, but where it is dark. The rapid exploitation of a good model system is far more profitable than painful investigation of an intractable virus, no matter how important.

Until 1933 when it was shown that influenza could be transmitted to ferrets and also adapted to mice, this virus was scarcely studied. The really big leap forward, however, was made with the demonstration of growth in embryonated eggs through the work first of Goodpasture and later Burnet. Embryonated eggs are those that have been fertilized by a rooster, as distinguished from the ordinary breakfast egg, which hopefully has not. In some ways the egg host has proved ideal. (1) Eggs are available in virtually unlimited quantity. (2) They can be raised in minimum space in incubators, and hundreds or even thousands of individual animals can be grown and handled with relative ease. (3) They are available from parents that are inbred, and hence eggs are relatively uniform genetically. (4) The environment is naturally constant. One need control only temperature and humidity. The inside of the egg has little contact with the outside world in the sense that it needs no food beyond its own stored supplies and does not excrete to the outside. (5) The egg ordinarily comes from the hen with the contents sterile. Hence one can study influenza, for example, without the complications of the adventitious viruses and bacteria of ordinary laboratory animals. (6) It is quite easy to introduce the virus into the egg and to harvest it later. (7) The chick embryo does not produce antibodies, avoiding many complications present in adult animals. (8) The developing chick offers a complete set of tissues and biochemical metabolic pathways; furthermore these change during development and thus present an even wider variety of environments than the adult.

Introduced into the egg at ten days of incubation, influenza multiplies rapidly, and large yields can be obtained after only about two more days. The egg can also be used for the assay of certain strains of the virus that kill it or, better, produce countable pocks or lesions on the chorioallantoic membrane (CAM). It has been shown that flu goes through a definable cycle of reproduction. Soon after the discovery that the egg was a good host came the development of hemagglutination as an extremely simple assay. With these discoveries a giant step in the study of animal viruses was taken; the field proliferated enormously. The basic discoveries rapidly made within this model system laid the foundation for most of modern animal virus research. Although tissue culture methods have proved in many ways more advantageous, embryonated eggs are still used in enormous numbers for the commercial production of viral vaccines.

Bacterial Virus Culture

The importance of simple cultural techniques is nowhere more elegantly demonstrated than with the work on bacterial viruses. In the 1930's, because of the work of Burnet, Schlesinger, and, particularly,

Max Delbrück, the d'Herelle "lytic agent" came to be accepted as a virus capable of infecting the cells of bacteria. Attention was more and more focused on a single group of seven T-phages which differed in many properties but which had as a common host the easily cultivated *Escherichia coli*, strain B. The fact that phages offered a model system for study of the basic phenomenon of reproduction was the first attraction for Delbrück and his followers. That bacteriophages paved the way for the study of viruses as biological objects and, by extension, as agents of disease was a not unexpected bonus.

There are many reasons why the phage system is ideal. (1) The host bacterium is a single-celled organism. When it is infected with a virus the subsequent events are localized in that cell and not, as with any animal or plant, spread in unknown ways through a myriad of various cell types, many of which may have no real role in viral reproduction. (2) These bacterial cells can be cultivated—in the instances that are of interest to us here—with simple equipment and in biochemically defined growth media. (3) The growth is under complete environmental control. (4) The cells may be grown in virtually unlimited numbers. A thousand embryonated eggs can be handled, as can a thousand mice, but with some strain on the facilities and budget and disposition of the investigator. It is much simpler to grow a hundred billion bacteria in a small flask; the process requires only a few hours and the cost is negligible. If, on the other hand, one wants pounds of bacteria, even that is feasible in readily available equipment. (5) Far more important, the bacteria, unlike any of the more complex hosts, can be obtained genetically quite uniform, since they are haploid. (That is, a culture can be started from a single organism without mating, and therefore all of the progeny, barring mutations, will be identical with this parent.) (6) The life cycle of the host cell is short; *Escherichia coli*, the most studied host, divides every 20 to 30 minutes under ordinary laboratory conditions. The life cycle of the virus is even shorter, as a rule, with multiplication by a factor of about 100 occurring in 15–30 minutes, depending on the host, the virus, and the conditions. (7) The infection of bacteria by viruses is simplicity itself, under proper conditions. One merely mixes the virus with susceptible cells in vigorous growth, and they promptly become infected, by a direct process of collision and attachment. (8) Techniques have been devised by which one can study either the progeny from a single infected cell or the population derived from infection of billions or even thousands of billions of cells. (9) It is feasible to prepare substantial quantities of viruses—gram quantities, for example—or of any intermediates or enzymes whose properties are of interest. (10) In addition to the preceding, because of the great simplicity and accuracy of the assay, which we shall consider later, biological studies are ideally simple. To summarize, then, phages are viruses whose cultural conditions can be idealized; quantitative experiments are possible and can be approached through many disciplines, from mathematics through genetics to biochemistry. One can easily wax lyrical by hindsight over this field of scientific investigation which had lain fallow for nearly two decades and which came to importance largely because of the vision of a few people, one of whom, Max Delbrück, was an evangelist.

Animal Viruses—Tissue Culture

As I have indicated already, the chief obstacle to the study of plant and animal viruses was for a time the lack of an ideal culture system for laboratory experimentation. The multicellular intact animal or plant is quite beyond our scientific comprehension at present even in the simplest instances. Work in the animal virus field, then, although of primary interest to us because of our anthropocentric outlook, bogged down because one knew neither where to start nor how to proceed. The first question was clarified through work with the vastly simpler bacterial virus system, in which the nature of the viral life cycle was described in quite detailed mathematical, biophysical, and biochemical terms. The question of how to proceed with animal viruses was really answered only with practical methods of tissue culture. Had the animal cell host technique been developed before the discovery of the bacterial virus system, we might never have needed it. But even at present the just plain day-to-day operations necessary in work with animal viruses in tissue culture systems are an order of magnitude more complicated, and the relative times of each aspect of the reproductive cycle are about an order of magnitude greater than is the case with phage. Full many a scientist, most of whom were born to blush unseen in dark, unfathomed caves of well-lighted, air-conditioned laboratories, contributed to the knowledge of tissue culture, but the man who led us into the modern era was John Enders. For his pioneering work with viruses in tissue culture, he received the Nobel Prize, with eminent justification, in 1954.

In theory, tissue culture is simple. One reduces a tissue to individual cells or small clumps and puts the resulting suspension into a suitable nutrient with a pleasant environment (Figure 4·3). How easy it sounds. The first thing that makes this process ten times more complicated than the culture of bacteria is bacteria. Tissue cells grow very slowly, and the gunk in which they thrive makes a virtual garden of delights for many bacteria. With careful technique and judicious use of antibiotics this problem was overcome. It took years to learn how to take a complex tissue and reduce it to its individual cellular components without important damage to the cells. The trick is to mince the tissue finely and then treat the *brei* with the enzyme trypsin, which, when applied skillfully, unglues the cells from each other without damage.

"A suitable nutrient" is one of those phrases like the "by the usual transformations" of the mathematical text. Many talented men have wrestled with this problem for years. It is obvious that in the intact animal fantastically complex mixtures of fluids are sloshing around. To simulate these in the test tube we have had to make up veritable witches' brews of amino acids, peptides, vitamins, minerals, purines, pyrimidines, trace elements, and sugars. Media intended for long-term healthy growth, as distinguished from media that merely allow cells to survive for a while, almost always contain a magic ingredient or two, usually serum and/or embryo extract. In other words the scientist puts in everything he can think of and then turns to the living animal to supply those ingredients that he has not been able to think of or cannot supply. Moreover, these factors must be present in exact balance; the pH must be just so and must be monitored with the aid of an indicator (for example, phenol red). "Environment" is another nice word. The first thing is that the glassware must be fanatically clean; the slightest trace of certain metals or of detergents, for example, is disastrous. A suitable atmosphere must be available, and in the interests of keeping the pH constant as the cells metabolize this often must be a balanced mixture of air and CO_2 supplied at just the right rate. The temperature may be critical, and even brief exposure to a lower temperature, as room temperature, may be fatal.

Tissue culture is not a technique to undertake in the garage or for a few quick experiments. But the methods *have* been worked out; most of the ingredients, including even completely made-up media, are available commercially—for a price that will curl your hair. The experiments made possible by these techniques, however, completely justify the trouble and expense.

Even more important than the mass culture of viruses is the use of tissue culture for diagnosis and assay. Through laboratory tissue culture, the field of animal virus research has virtually exploded in a manner that did not seem possible only a decade ago. The fundamental properties of the viruses, the description of their life cycles, and the biochemistry of their reproduction, and so forth, are appearing in the literature at an unbelievable rate. Nothing, in fact, could serve as a better demonstration of the fruits of basic research than these developments of techniques which for years had no practical value.

Summary

The take-home lesson from this chapter is that progress in the study of various kinds of viruses and of their chemical, physical, or biological properties has occurred very largely in those areas in which satisfactory cultural techniques have been developed. The definition of *satisfactory*, however, depends on the virus and the goals of research.

4

The Assay of Viruses

To STUDY any phenomenon in modern biology, the first step is to devise ways of doing quantitative work, in this case to determine the amount of virus by some sort of assay (titration). Even the development of cultural methods is possible only if one knows which of two experiments gives more virus. Hence, in general, the development of culture methods and assay techniques must go hand in hand. Any of a number of physical or chemical properties could be used to determine the amount of virus in a purified preparation. In general, however, this is the end result rather than where one begins. Far more important is the fact that such methods can tell us only the amount of *viral material*—perhaps the amount of protein, or nucleic acid, or the number of particles. When we are considering the virus as a biological object, we want to know the number of *infectious* particles. A viral assay, then, almost always involves some sort of estimation of this number. The requirements of an assay are that it be simple, quick, and quantitative. As in the previous chapters we shall follow a semihistorical exposition to illustrate the development of this area.

The Minimum Infectious Dose

Even as we can simply bring the natural host into the laboratory to culture a virus, we can often use it for assay. In theory we can attempt to infect individual host animals, plants, and insects with increasing dilution of the virus until a dilution is reached at which no infection occurs. In this way, one might think the minimum infectious dose could be established as a unit. As with most simple statements this one is fraught with complications. Biological variation, the principal demon of that level of purgatory in which biologists have chosen to dwell, promptly takes command. As we know all too well, in the Brownie troop, family, classroom, or barracks, a disease that is rampant will hit some people and leave others untouched. This is likewise true of any population in which one tries to introduce a virus deliberately. The reasons are many. Some of them have been discussed in the second chapter. But assuming controlled external conditions, such as lack of previous exposure and uniform nutrition, one will still have degrees of susceptibility. The variables are too numerous to control in any real situation. The use of carefully inbred strains of animals is most important, of course, and where laboratory mice or embryonated eggs can be used, the minimum infectious dose concept can be reduced from a nightmare to a slight headache. Even with an idealized, perfectly homogeneous population of susceptible animals, however, the problem is far from solved. Let's assume that an infectious dose is one viral particle, applied to the right cell. We can still have trouble. To illustrate this, suppose that we have a flask containing one virus per milliliter of solution and that we are going to take a set of one milliliter samples from it and inject each into an animal. Will each animal get a virus? One is apt to reply, "Obviously." But, no! We are dealing, here, with a distribution of discrete (indivisible) objects, you either have one or more viral particles—an infection—or none. A quite famous mathematician, Poisson, considered the problem of the distribution of a small average number of discrete objects into samples long before viruses were ever heard of. Take the situation in which we are administering terminally diluted doses of virus containing an average of one infectious particle per dose. The Poisson distribution states that 37 per cent of such samples will contain no viral particles, 37 per cent will contain one particle per dose, and the remaining 26 per cent will contain more than a single particle. If you find this hard to believe, it is simple to try. Take any number of boxes of the same size—for example, egg crating. Take the same number of marbles and toss them randomly until all marbles have fallen into one or another of the boxes. If you are reasonably careful to randomize your throwing you will find that your distribution of marbles comes ever closer to the Poisson prediction the more times you repeat the experiment.

The meaning of this for our present purposes is that even if we do achieve, by chance, the ideal dilution which has an average of one virus per dose, only 63 per cent (those that get one plus those that get more than one particle) of the animals will be infected. Or, to put it the other way, if we want to decide which of a series of dilutions contains an average of one virus per dose, we should look for the dilution that infects 63 per cent of the animals. Obviously, then, our original idea of looking for the last dilution that can cause an infection is very naïve, since even a dilution containing only one particle per ten doses or even one per hundred doses can cause an occasional infection in a population of millions, but in a quite unpredictable way for any individual host.

Virologists long ago understood the foregoing situation intuitively, and hence developed the idea of the LD50, ID50, or TCD50 (the *lethal dose* or the *infectious dose* which infects 50 per cent of the animals or *tissue cultures*) as being far more useful than the last dilution that could infect or the last dilution that killed all animals injected. Had these virologists been more mathematically sophisticated they might have chosen instead the LD63.

There is one more unfortunate fact which now rears its head. Animals, even eggs, even bottles of tissue culture, cost money, take time to prepare, and require space. It should be obvious that the assay by ID50, for example, will be the more accurate the more animals one uses per dilution. But one has to be practical, which is to say that he usually has to settle for eight or perhaps six or maybe even four animals per dilution and dilutions by greater steps than the ideal, perhaps even by factors of ten. The assay becomes less accurate, obviously, but at least feasible to perform. There are mathematical tricks (The Reed-Muench method, for example) which are commonly used to squeeze the maximum statistical advantage from the small samples.

Thus, determination of the ID50 or LD50 always represents a compromise with practicality and is inherently quite inaccurate. But it has one undeniable advantage. *It works!* If a virus causes an infection of any laboratory host or discernible damage (CPE or *cyto*pathogenic *e*ffect) in tubes of tissue culture, one can always apply the ID50 as an assay with the assurance that he is at least measuring the primary property of the virus—the ability to cause disease. It is frequently the only available method, and in skillful hands and with favorable conditions it can be most useful. This type of assay has beyond doubt been the mainstay of virology.

Linear Response

As even a fledgling biophysicist can tell you, one really wants a linear response assay for any phenomenon. In any situation in science, obviously, if twice the dose gives ten times the effect, one usually has only a very small range of dose over which response measurement is possible; and if twice the does gives only 5 per cent more effect, the accuracy of measurement of response becomes critical. The best is the situation in between, a linear response in which twice the dose gives twice the effect. With viruses, then, one would like ideally to be able to see the result of every infectious particle and to be able to count them by simply counting the infected animals or plants. This situation can be realized in theory if a small number of viral particles can be introduced into a huge population of infectable hosts in such a way that every particle will find a host and the infection is *not* passed from one host to another. This is practically impossible with mice or eggs, but is quite feasible in several systems.

Local Lesions in Tobacco Plants

The first viral system in which a response of the linear type was developed involved, again, our old friend TMV. F. O. Holmes found in

1929—a year not otherwise noted as a time of rejoicing—that *Nicotiana glutinosa*, a relative of the common tobacco plant, showed localized leaf lesions when rubbed gently with a suitable dilution of the tobacco mosaic virus. It was found that the number of necrotic lesions (Figure 4·1) was proportional, roughly, to the amount of virus applied. One can indeed estimate the amount of virus by counting the lesions and multiplying by the dilution factor for the sample that gave this number of viral infections. The important difference between this kind of assay and the ID50 or LD50 assay is that one has here a huge number of available cells in the surface of even a single leaf. These cells, are, to a very rough approximation, equally susceptible to TMV, and

Figure 4·1. Assay of tobacco mosaic virus by rubbing successive dilutions (1:1; 1:3.16, 1:10, 1:100, 1:1000) on leaves of *Nicotiana glutinosa*. [Picture supplied by Dr. F. O. Holmes, Rockefeller University, New York.]

the infection of even a single cell results in a spreading effect of the multiplying virus into neighboring susceptible cells with the eventual production of a quite readily visible area of damage. Didactically it would be nice if this situation represented a true linear response, but the complications are repulsive even today after some thirty-five years of study. Leaf susceptibility varies even within a single plant. Within limits, however, this is a good quantitative assay and there is no doubt that its availability influenced Stanley in his choice of a virus to purify and hence influenced the entire development of modern virology.

But there is an ancillary aspect to the local lesion response which we must consider. I have said that each such lesion is the result of an original infection by a single viral particle. We shall justify this statement later. But if true—and, again, with TMV the case is weak in retrospect—this means that all of the viral particles in each lesion are the descendants of a single particle. That is to say, they are a *clone* (genetically identical with the original particle except for random mutations). Using a lesion as a starting stock, one can proceed in research with the assurance that he has at least begun with a single genetic entity. It is possible to argue similarly that a viral stock is genetically homogeneous when it results from the infection of a host at terminal dilution. Such an infection presumably resulted from a single viral particle, but the argument is weak.

Plaque Assay—Bacterial Viruses

With the bacterial viruses, an assay of similar type perfected by A. Gratia, an Italian, in 1936, is the key technique in the whole area of bacterial viral research. As it is now done, one begins with a simple Petri plate containing a suitable nutrient solution for bacteria. The nutrient has been immobilized by the inert jelling agent agar (a crude polysaccharide derived from seaweed). An important characteristic of dilute agar solutions is that they melt only near the boiling point of water, but they then stay unjelled upon cooling until near body temperature (37°C). A small additional amount of nutrient agar is melted and cooled to 45°C. A concentrated culture of perhaps 100 million host bacteria plus a few—perhaps a hundred or so—viruses can now be mixed in this *top agar* without harm and poured onto the plate where the mixture will promptly jell, more or less immobilizing the suspension of virus and bacteria. Each virus soon finds a host cell. The chances at the outset of a host cell being infected by more than one virus particle are nil, since there are about a million host cells for every virus.

Each infected host cell produces a hundred or so viruses which migrate to adjacent host cells (members of the original suspension or their progeny, since the uninfected cells also multiply rapidly on the plate). The result after only a few hours is that there is a lawn of bacteria on the plate with occasional clear areas resulting from the destruction of a group of cells by the progeny of a single viral particle (Figure 4·2).

The important fact is that here we have a true linear assay covering a wide range (to several thousand plaques) with salutary accuracy. The technique is simple, the time involved short, and the cost trivial. A plate yielding an assay accurate to about 15 per cent costs ten cents, more or less. A typical mouse assay (six mice per dilution with four dilutions tried) would cost about five dollars, take several days, and the accuracy would not be a subject for decent discussion among molecular biologists. If you are a physicist, or even a chemist, you may find the idea of an assay with a 15 per cent error revolting in the extreme. After all, the speed of light is known to a dozen significant figures. But in biology this methodology is so much better than what preceded it that a life science revolution was born as a result.

We should also remember that the plaque contains the progeny from a single viral particle, a genetic clone. In practice it is very simple indeed to prepare such a pure stock by carefully stabbing a single plaque with a sterile needle and infecting a culture of susceptible bacteria by dipping the needle into it. In a few hours one can thus prepare a genetically homogeneous stock (except for random mutations) containing perhaps a billion viral particles per milliliter. We might also point out that the host bacteria can be easily cloned also by standard techniques of microbiology. The most-studied system of *E. coli* and seven T-phages was isolated from sewage samples by these techniques. More can be found at will. In the bacterial virus system the bugaboo of biological variation is thus reduced to a minimum.

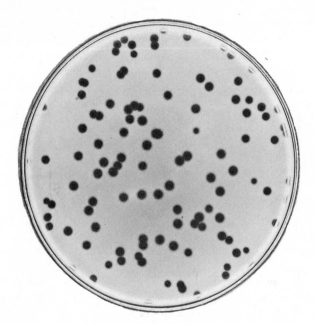

Figure 4·2. Assay of bacteriophage by plating on a lawn of *E. coli*.

Lesion Assays of Animal Viruses

It was noticed first by Goodpasture and his collaborators (1931) that fowl pox virus applied at an appropriate dilution causes countable lesions on the chorioallantoic membrane of the embryonated egg. This technique, although far less convenient and accurate than the plaque assay for bacteriophage, gave considerable impetus to study of a number of viruses—for example, vaccinia, ectromelia, and herpes—which have this property of producing discrete lesions. But the principal use came with the experiments of Burnet, in the 1940's, on certain strains of influenza that can be simply and inexpensively (ten cents per egg) assayed in this manner with an accuracy of some 50 per cent. Again this may sound revoltingly inaccurate, but it is a great improvement over end-point techniques and gave the field a considerable boost. The cell population of the individual membrane is reasonably uniform, the pock or lesion is a clone, and the assay is linear over a limited range.

After the development of the tissue culture methods by Enders and others, a deliberate application of phage techniques by R. Dulbecco proved the possibility of lesion-type assays for animal viruses. As usually done today, a monolayer of tissue culture on glass is overlaid with agar-nutrient containing virus. With something over a hundred viruses it has proved possible (Figure 4·3) to find host cells that give plaques—spots of discernible cytopathogenic damage. There is little doubt, in fact, that the current tremendous burgeoning of animal virus research has come largely from these developments in methodology which permit quantitative experimentation, even though the techniques are much more expensive and time-consuming and technically more difficult than those used in bacteriophage research.

Figure 4·3. Assay of measles virus by plating successive 10-fold dilutions on monolayers of monkey kidney tissue culture. [From G. D. Hsiung, *Proceedings of the Society for Experimental Biology and Medicine*, 98: 68, 1958.]

Indirect Methods

Particular properties of certain viruses otherwise difficult to assay have frequently proved useful. *Hemagglutination* (HA) describes the ability of the myxo viruses (influenza, Newcastle) to clump various animal red blood cells. The last dilution causing this effect contains one HA unit/ml. This extremely simple, rapid, inexpensive technique gave enormous impetus to influenza research in the 1950's. Specific antisera, usually prepared in rabbits, often react with viruses to produce quantitative effects observable by one or another of a number of special techniques. These serological methods (especially complement fixation) have been widely used for diagnostic purposes and to some extent as assays. Various physical measurements have proved useful. One that never fails to appeal to the student is the use of the electron microscope to visualize and hence actually to count the particles. The complications, however, are considerable; this is *no assay*.

With all of these indirect measurements it must be understood that one is not necessarily estimating the biologically active infective virus. To cite a particularly egregious case, the best TMV preparations contain 25,000 particles countable in the electron microscope for every infectious one. Not infrequently, of course, one *wants* to know the total number of particles, infectious or not; and in such a case, measurement of some property other than infectability is necessary.

Summary

We have seen that the assay of viruses is possible by a wide variety of techniques, varying from the often crude but at least sure method of LD50 or ID50 in host animals to rather elegant and, by biological standards, accurate techniques of plaque or lesion assay. Viral research has progressed almost directly as a result of the development, in each of the main areas, of simple, inexpensive, linear-response assays. That viral research has contributed so significantly to molecular biology can be traced largely to the use of controllable, quantitative model systems.

5

The Purification of Viruses

THE STUDY of viruses as biological objects rather than as agents of disease proceeded along two lines, one biological the other biochemical. Before studies of the biological properties (see next chapter) could proceed very far, it was necessary to know something about the physical and chemical properties of viruses. For most such studies a highly purified preparation is essential. With this understanding, Wendell M. Stanley set about purifying TMV in the 1930's. In general, the purification of viruses is facilitated in a virus-host system for which at least some of the following statements are true: (1) The virus can be assayed quickly, simply, and accurately. (2) Viral culture is easy. (3) The yields of virus are large. (4) The properties of the virus allow it to be separated readily from host cell components.

Every virologist soon learns that each new virus must be treated as an individual. The fact that few generalizations are possible is especially true in the art of viral purification. We can thus do no more here than indicate the historical approaches and some of the more successful and more widely applicable modern methods.

TMV, the first virus to be purified, offered an almost unique combination of advantageous properties, and Stanley's success was attributable, as is so often the case in biological research, very largely to his choice of this nearly ideal system. His preliminary work seemed to confirm the opinions of others that the virus was probably a protein; he therefore set about purifying it by techniques developed for protein purification based mainly on differential precipitation by salts, acids, and chemical agents. These methods are tedious and extremely crude by present-day standards, but they had one characteristic that cannot be gainsaid—they succeeded. Stanley was able to produce highly concentrated and purified virus which could, in fact, be crystallized. These were not true crystals, since they had only two-dimensional symmetry, but the fact that they could be obtained and that the viral activity remained after repeated recrystallization convinced Stanley that the living virus was a chemical molecule. His analyses indicated that TMV was a protein, and it was only some two years later that Bawden and Pirie demonstrated the presence of 0.5 per cent of phosphorus. TMV has an unusually small amount of phosphorus, but this betokens the real heart of the virus, the nucleic acid. There is no doubt at all that these discoveries, coming on top of the identification of enzymes as protein molecules, changed our entire outlook on the nature of life and gave great impetus to the present era of molecular biology—the explanation of biological phenomena in chemical and physical terms.

Encouraged by Stanley's success, other scientists soon attempted the purification of a number of plant, animal, and bacterial viruses. Few plant viruses occur in yields as high as TMV (a gram or more per liter of plant juice), but with modern techniques even a small fraction (perhaps down to 5 to 10 mg per liter) of this phenomenal initial concentration has sufficed. Among animal viruses, only some of those causing insect disease seem to offer even comparable yields. Those for which egg cultivation has been favorable (for example, influenza) generally yield only about one milligram per ten milliliters of allantoic fluid—that is, per egg. Many years later, polio virus was purified and crystallized, even though yields were only 50–100 *micro*grams per liter of raw fluid. The bacterial viruses are frequently very easy to prepare in quantity, and those most studied, for example, T2, can be obtained with raw titers of 10^{12} viral particles per milliliter, approximately a gram of virus per liter. In many instances it has been necessary and possible to start with far less favorable yields than the ideal.

Preliminary Treatment

Nearly all viral preparations contain considerable amounts of cellular debris. A usual first step is to remove this material by a fairly crude filtration, perhaps through diatomaceous earth, and/or by low-speed centrifugation. Sometimes the mixture at this stage is treated with proteolytic enzymes or nucleases because viruses seem to have been designed to resist these enzymes. The enzyme treatment, therefore, serves to rid the raw preparation of troublesome junk. Other procedures, such as solvent extraction to remove lipid-containing debris, may be used in certain instances.

A most important aspect of any purification is careful bookkeeping, by assay of every fraction at each stage, to ensure that one is not throwing out the baby with the bathwater or killing it with kindness. The object of purification, after all, is segregation of the minimum material with maximum viral infectivity and the ideal of having finally only the virus itself. Thus at every step, one usually calculates the *specific infectivity* by dividing the viral titer by the total nitrogen (as determined by any of a number of standard methods, such as Kjeldahl analysis) or the dry weight or some such parameter designed to quantitate the total material present. The final objective, of course, is maximum specific infectivity.

Concentration and Further Purification

The next problem is almost always to reduce the preparation to easily handled volumes, to concentrate the virus, preferably without loss of titer and preferably with the elimination of further extraneous material. This can be accomplished in a variety of ways.

PRECIPITATION.   Following the lead of Stanley, a very common treatment is precipitation of the virus in the cold by the addition of any of various highly soluble salts (typically ammonium sulfate) or miscible solvents (typically alcohol or acetone). The precipitate is then resuspended, usually in buffer, for further purification. In general, however, these methods have proved rather destructive of virus and have been supplanted by such operations as centrifugation or selective absorption of the virus.

CENTRIFUGATION.   In order to centrifuge a virus one must be able to achieve speeds in the range of 12,000 rpm to 30,000 rpm. In the early days (the 1930's) there were only a very few such machines, and they were used for analytical work, not viral preparation. The principle of centrifugation is extremely simple. If a mixture of dirt from the back yard is dumped into a bucket of water, some material, being of lesser density than water, will float—for example, wood chips, dead beetles, and plastic baby toys. Other more dense substances will sink. Under slightly idealized conditions one can see that the stones will form the bottom layer, above it sand, then the dirt particles, and finally, perhaps settling only after several hours, the clay. In other words, objects will settle out in an order determined partly by their density and shape but mainly by their size when they have similar densities. As everyone knows, usually from a few disastrous trials as a child, water can be forced toward the bottom of even an upside down bucket by swinging the bucket in a circle—in this case the centrifugal force acts as an increased gravitational force. So it is with the ultracentrifuge, except that the particles with which one deals are much smaller and hence require a very strong centrifugal field to sediment them.

In 1949 a development occurred, however, which completely revolutionized centrifugation and hence viral concentration and purification. This was the production of the Spinco (now Beckman) ultracentrifuge. Basing his ideas on years of experimentation at the Rockefeller Institute and previous designs by Svedberg and others, Ed Pickels, in conjunction with associates who were mechanical and electrical engineers of great skill, produced an ultracentrifuge that was capable of speeds up to 40,000 rpm and hence centrifugal forces of up to 125,000 times gravity. In my opinion this machine has done more than any other single instrument to advance the study of viruses, yet Pickels has received almost no attention for these remarkable achievements. Previously ultracentrifuges had to be run in the subbasement behind three-foot-thick walls of reinforced concrete. They were individually built; the scientists who operated them were considered slightly insane. Centrifuges required constant attention, the technical skill of a Kettering, a willingness to spend most of your time flat on your back in a puddle of oil doing plumbing and mechanical repairs. Explosions that wrecked the machine were to be expected at fairly regular intervals. The Spinco preparative centrifuge, for contrast, is about the size of a family washing machine (Fig. 5·1), and anyone can learn to run it in ten minutes. The equipment can be set in a corner of the laboratory, and explosions and other mishaps are of historical interest only; the centrifuge I currently use, for example, has been going for ten years or more, in constant use, with only two or three routine maintenance visits a year from the manufacturer.

Figure 5·1. Beckman-Spinco preparative ultracentrifuge (with the cover removed). At the upper left is the armor-plate steel protective chamber. The drive motor is below it hidden by the electronic control panel. (*Top right*) Refrigeration unit. (*Bottom right*) Vacuum pump. [Photo supplied by Spinco Division, Beckman Instruments, Palo Alto, California.]

A number of other centrifuges are now also available which are capable of somewhat lesser speeds, still adequate to produce pellets of many viruses. As a result, centrifugation is now almost invariably the basis of concentration and purification procedures for viral preparations. Particulate debris is removed at low speeds; the virus is then pelleted at high speeds, leaving smaller molecules in the supernatant fluid. Several cycles of such *differential centrifugation* usually serve to concentrate the virus a hundredfold or more and at the same time free it of impurities both larger and smaller.

DENSITY GRADIENT CENTRIFUGATION. An important advance in the technique of centrifugation was made by M. K. Brakke in 1953. Brakke conceived the idea of stabilizing a band of material during centrifugation by layering sucrose solutions of different concentrations (and hence densities) in the tube at the outset. The most dense layer is at the bottom, the next less dense above it, and so on. The mixture to be centrifuged is layered on the top (Figure 5·2). This process differs from the ordinary centrifugation in several particulars. The particles or macromolecules are subject to a centrifugal field which tends to separate them as usual. Since the mixture is in a layer or band, each component travels in a separate band. But in addition the solvent of increasing density tends to sharpen these bands. The particles are also subjected to increasing viscosity of the successive layers of sucrose. Thus several parameters operate which may cause the various components to behave rather differently from usual. This often leads to excellent separation of materials that are next to impossible to distinguish in ordinary centrifugation.

A very important variant of the density gradient technique was developed by M. Meselson, F. Stahl, and J. Vinograd. In their method the gradient is *formed* by the centrifugation as shown in Figure 5·2. A salt of a heavy metal with high solubility (usually cesium chloride or sulfate) is made into a quite concentrated solution in water or a buffer. The intense centrifugal field causes the formation of a density gradient right in the spinning tube because the inorganic salt is partially centrifuged. After some hours of spinning, the gradient reaches *equilibrium*. At some point the density of the solvent and particles (for example, viruses) exactly match. All of the particles eventually collect in a very narrow band at this point, the width of the band being determined by diffusion. The important thing is that the given particle no longer moves, depending on its size and shape, as in other forms of centrifugation, but comes to rest at a place determined solely by its density. Particles can be separated whose density differs in the third decimal place. They are ordinarily isolated by punching a hole in the tube and collecting successive drops. These extremely powerful techniques are now frequently employed as a final step in viral purification.

ADSORPTION. Sometimes it is not practical to centrifuge a virus. Potential pathogens might be dispersed as aerosols by leakage. It may also be awkward to handle the large amounts of material necessary because of low initial titer, or it may be that one simply wants large quantities—grams—of a virus. For such purposes, adsorption techniques are very useful. Without going into detail, it may be said that a wide variety of substances, varying from finely divided charcoal to

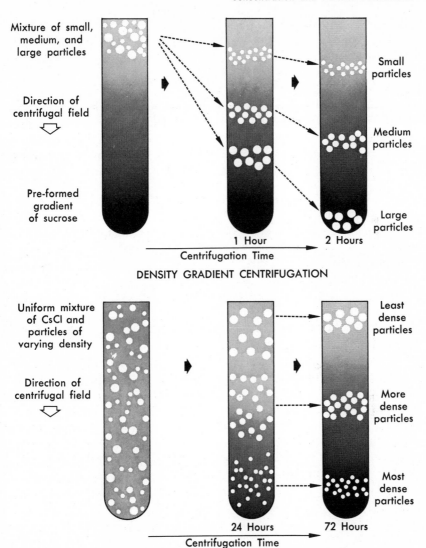

Mixture of small, medium, and large particles

Direction of centrifugal field ⬇

Pre-formed gradient of sucrose

Small particles

Medium particles

Large particles

1 Hour   2 Hours

Centrifugation Time

DENSITY GRADIENT CENTRIFUGATION

Uniform mixture of CsCl and particles of varying density

Direction of centrifugal field ⬇

Least dense particles

More dense particles

Most dense particles

24 Hours   72 Hours

Centrifugation Time

EQUILIBRIUM DENSITY GRADIENT CENTRIFUGATION

Figure 5·2. Schematic representation of hydrodynamic and equilibrium density gradient centrifugation.

clays and synthetic ion exchange resins, have the property of adsorbing to their surfaces all kinds of soluble materials (*solutes*) such as salts or sugars or large molecules such as proteins or even particles, as viruses. The strength of adsorption varies from adsorbent to adsorbent and solute to solute. It can be controlled very exactly, usually, by varying the *p*H, the combination of solvents, or the ionic strength (roughly the concentration of ionic charges in the solution). Often one can adsorb out an impurity or adsorb a desired substance, as a virus, preferentially. In the latter instance, by changing the conditions the virus can again be released (eluted). This procedure, named chromatography, is often very selective and gentle; it can be used to purify often with considerable concentration. We use routinely, for example, a chromatographic procedure that enables us to concentrate bacteriophage T2 fifty to a hundredfold with over 90 per cent recovery from a quite crude lysate after only a treatment to remove large debris. The modified cellulose (the adsorbent) suspended in a buffer is poured into a vertical tube where it is held by a perforated plate at the bottom. The viral suspension is then poured in at the top. Many impurities flow through, the virus sticks. By increasing the salt concentration in a later wash, the virus is released and flows out as a concentrate from the bottom of the tube. A rather similar technique allows one "sieve" TMV on agar granules and obtain extremely pure virus *in about fifteen minutes,* starting from the leaves on the infected plant. This virus is probably as pure as, and in some ways far better than, the best material Stanley obtained after weeks of work! These procedures have the advantages of speed, wide application (though to one degree or another they have to be worked out individually for every virus) and unbelievable simplicity.

MISCELLANEOUS PROCEDURES.   Many other methods have been developed for use in the purification of viruses; many have been tailormade to suit individual viruses and hosts. Without giving details we might at least mention adsorption and re-elution from red blood cells; concentration by evaporation, pervaporation, or dialysis against a water absorbent; continuous flow centrifugation; electrophoresis; solvent extraction; selective filtration (seldom practicable); acid or heat denaturation of impurities. Very often one finds a particular host or part of a host in which the virus occurs naturally in high concentration or under conditions that favor concentration or purification.

Viral Purity—The Meaning of "Purity"

Everyone is inclined to think that he knows exactly what is meant by purity. Something is *pure* when it consists of just that something and nothing else. Thus "pure milk"—to use a term in common parlance and having great currency in the advertising profession—contains milk and no dead mice. But actually milk, as anyone knows on a little reflection, is a complete food and hence a fantastic mixture of water, fats, proteins, salts, sugars, vitamins, and about everything else biological. Even the best milk contains many bacteria. Is limburger cheese or pizza a pure food? But enough of this sport. In science surely we know exactly what we mean by such terms. A virus is pure when it is a virus and nothing else contaminates it.

Unfortunately we have to back off for a minute from even this unexceptionable 100 per cent American statement. Almost every virus is extremely unhappy unless it is in water. So, in actuality, "pure virus" is a suspension consisting of over 90 per cent if not 99 per cent plus of water (99 per cent water is pretty pure water in some sections of the world). And almost every virus is unhappy in the extreme unless the water, which is to say also the viral particle, contains a fair amount of a few salts plus a little buffer to keep the pH reasonable. As every virologist knows, most viruses are stable only if they have proteins in the suspension with them. One might easily decide that a "pure virus" is a pretty miscellaneous collection of stuff, albeit of known composition. It is beginning to sound, as Humpty Dumpty said, like a question of who is to be the master, we or the words.

But it is not as simple as that. We may decide to cut through all of this obfuscation and say that the virus is the infecting agent. The suspension may contain water and salts, perhaps, but the *biological* material is only virus. It would be nice if we could agree even on this. Unfortunately we now know, as we shall see in more detail later, that the real infectious part of a virus is the nucleic acid. The protein is just a coat that protects the nucleic acid against the slings and arrows of outrageous fortune and has, in many cases, properties that enable the nucleic acid to get into the host cell. So is the protein an impurity? As a biologist you say, "Certainly not. It is a part of the virus. It is necessary for it to infect and to remain stable—that is, retain its biological identity." Unfortunately many viruses require magnesium or calcium to remain stable or to infect cells. Are these part of the virus? And some viruses contain proteins *inside* with the nucleic acid and also diamines. They may vary in quantity considerably from particle to particle, but many virologists have a sneaking suspicion that they may be quite important. If you are confused, you are in good company.

"Purity" for electron microscopy is quite different from chemical purity. Macromolecular homogeneity is entirely different from biological "purity." Probably no two biological objects are ever *identical* in terms of chemical minutiae or genetically. Mutants always exist even though we may not have identified them. One can, then, define "purity" only in terms dictated by the particular purpose.

Summary

Starting from fairly harsh chemical techniques, viral purification now consists largely of the application of physical methods such as differential and gradient centrifugation, selective adsorption, and solvent extraction, plus certain "tricks" devised to suit the particular system. Viral purity must be defined in terms of the purpose.

6

The Chemical and Physical Properties of Viruses

STUDY of the chemical and physical properties of viruses requires, in most instances, purified preparations. Actually the earliest information came from rather indirect observations, especially of such properties as the ability to pass filters of certain pore sizes, the ability to refract or scatter light in characteristic ways, the behavior of the viral particles in the ultracentrifuge, the observation that viral suspensions were inactivated by agents known to denature proteins. These slightly arcane characteristics, however, had little appeal at first for the biologist, far less the public. One of the first properties to catch even scientific fancy consisted of the pictures of viral particles taken with the electron microscope. The actual physical appearance of a virus, then, is a good property to begin with.

Electron Microscopy

As a criterion of viral *purity,* the electron microscope has quite limited application. If the question is whether the preparation is contaminated with similar particles somehow distinguishable on the basis of size or morphology, the microscope can be very useful. This ordinarily applies to the final stages of purification. It can sometimes show us that the preparation contains broken or "ghost" particles. It can provide us with the most important relationship between the number of actual particles and the number of infectious units. The neophyte in biology, however, is universally convinced that if he can just *see* something he will know a lot about it. The structure of viral particles can, of course, be seen in the electron microscope.

GENERAL MORPHOLOGY. The theories of optics tell us that the limit of the resolving power of any microscope is set by the wavelength of the radiation used for "illumination." With the light microscope we are thus limited, for practical purposes, to a resolution of one-half the wavelength of blue light, or approximately 2,000Å. This means that viruses of diameter averaging some 100 mμ (millimicrons) (1,000Å) are just below the resolution limit.

The development of the electron microscope pretty well coincided in time with the early part of the modern virus era (the 1930's). With TMV the physical chemists told the virologists early that the particles of virus must be long and thin. The electron microscope (Figure 6·1) gave actual pictures of the particles showing indeed that they are rods

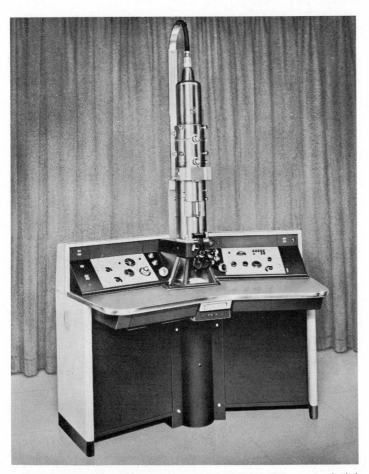

Figure 6·1. RCA electron microscope. Model EMU-3H. [Photo supplied by the Radio Corporation of America, Camden, New Jersey.]

of diameter 15 mμ and length 300 mμ (Figure 6·2). Thus the predictions of the physical chemists, derived from theoretical considerations of indirect measurements, were triumphantly vindicated. Other plant viruses were also shown to be rodlike (as potato X), but many were found to be apparently spherical (tomato bushy stunt, turnip yellow mosaic), also as predicted by physical measurements.

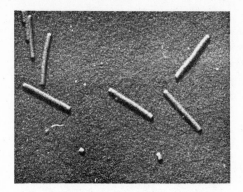

Figure 6·2. Tobacco mosaic virus rods as seen in the electron microscope (×45,000) after shadowing with uranium metal. [Photo supplied by Dr. R. C. Williams, Dept. of Molecular Biology, University of California, Berkeley, Calif.]

With the development of bacterial virology came the entertaining discovery (ca. 1942) that many of these viruses have shapes that have been variously described as tadpole or spermlike. At any rate they have roundish "heads" and appendages which were immediately and universally called "tails" with the implication that they are used for swimming. This red herring (if I may be pardoned) did not seriously mislead, but it was nearly ten years later that painstaking physical measurements by Frank Putnam showed that phages do not actively swim, but move simply by diffusion. This example is cited mainly to show that a picture may be worth 10,000 words, but it can be appallingly misleading, especially when teleologically interpreted. We now know, largely through electron microscopy, that bacterial viruses can range from these tadpole shapes (Figure 6·3) through simple "spherical" (actually polyhedral) shapes to rods, though the latter so far seem to be rare.

Visualization of animal viruses came later than the others, mainly because of the difficulties in obtaining sufficient quantities for adequate purification. This was, perhaps, fortunate, since by the time pictures were obtained one was attuned to the idea that viruses are nothing much to look at. Anyone who has seen an enlarged picture of a crab

Figure 6·3. Electron micrograph of bacteriophage T4. Uranium shadowed ×45,000. [Photo supplied by Dr. R. C. Williams, Dept. of Molecular Biology, University of California, Berkeley, Calif.]

louse has a good idea of why these creatures are disgusting and annoying. They *look* disgusting and annoying—all feet, hairy legs, and claws.
Even a nicely flagellated bacterium can, in enlargement, look vaguely
sinister. But nothing looks more harmless than a neatly geometrical
polio or influenza virus (Figure 6·4). In general most animal viruses
are of simple polyhedral morphology, although we now know that the
larger ones are more complex and that the largest ones—for example,
vaccinia—are brick-shaped (Figure 6·5) for reasons not yet clear.

Figure 6·4. Poliomyelitis virus as seen in the electron microscope after shadowing
with uranium (×73,000). [Photo supplied by Dr. R. C. Williams, Dept. of Molecular
Biology, University of California, Berkeley, Calif.]

Figure 6·5. Vaccinia virus as seen in the electron microscope after uranium shadowing (×54,000). [Photo supplied by Dr. R. C. Williams, Dept. of Molecular Biology, University of California, Berkeley, Calif.]

DETAILED MORPHOLOGY.   The detailed morphology of the viruses has not been worked out by electron microscopy alone. The reason for this is not, as one might suspect, a lack in the instrument. The actual problem is mainly one of contrast. The electron microscope works because various components of the objects scatter a uniform beam of electrons to various degrees, depending on their electron density and actual thickness. An atom of a heavy metal scatters far more effectively (is more electron dense) than one of carbon. Unfortunately biological objects are founded on carbon, hydrogen, oxygen, nitrogen, plus a little sulfur and phosphorus, all atoms with little and nearly identical scattering power. A principal additional complication derives from the fact that water also consists of hydrogen and oxygen and hence has scattering power which would completely swamp that of any specimen suspended in it. Air molecules would also scatter electrons. Thus the column of the electron microscope must operate in a high vacuum and the specimen must be completely dry. Glass slides or chambers, of course, would scatter the electron beam totally before it reached the specimen. So now we have two main problems; we must dry specimens completely without distorting them, and we must provide contrast. The problem of distortion-free drying of liquid suspensions was solved through techniques developed by T. F. Anderson and by Robley Williams, who has been a principal contributor to the electron microscopy of viruses. A second general technique, fixation and embedding in plastic followed by sectioning, is more applicable to tissues and hence to virus-host systems than to free virus.

The contrast enhancement required has been provided by three methods, all involving the selective addition of metals to provide greater electron scattering power. The first of these, also developed by Robley Williams, is *geometrically* selective and involves "shadowing"—depositing (in a high vacuum) an extremely thin film of metal—for example, platinum or uranium—on one side of the specimen. Parts of the specimens shield others from being coated, and a three-dimensional optical effect is created. This process has revealed much about the surface features of many viruses but unfortunately covers up the most intimate details of structure. More recently it has been possible, through the work of Porter, Hall, and others, to stain biological specimens somewhat selectively with any of various metal compounds, as osmic acid or lead salts. One can also stain "negatively," as with phosphotungstic acid. In this technique, the biological specimen becomes embedded in a matrix of the heavy metal compound which does not attach to it but which fills in empty spaces to give them high contrast. Oddly enough this unlikely-sounding technique provides the best resolution so far obtainable with free viruses (Figure 6·6).

Because of the artifacts of preparation, difficulties with contrast, and technical complications, the resolution of the final structural details has been greatly inferior to the 4–6 Å resolution obtainable with the best

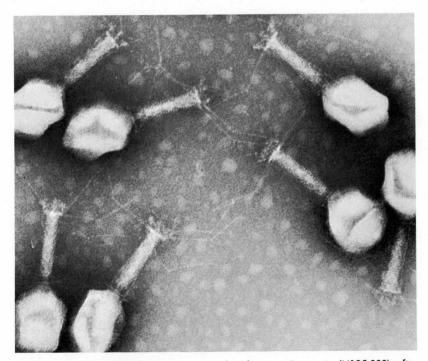

Figure 6·6. T4 bacteriophage as seen in the electron microscope (×185,000) after negative staining with phosphotungstic acid. [Photo supplied by E. Boy de la Tour and E. Kellenberger, Centre de Microscopie Electronique, University of Geneva, Switzerland. From *Virology*, New York: Academic Press, 1965, p. 419.]

electron microscopes; in fact, our present detailed knowledge has come through a combination of use of the electron microscope and of x-ray diffraction. We shall consider the results after we have discussed this technique.

X-Ray Diffraction

The x-ray, like visible light, is electromagnetic radiation but of extremely small wavelength (approximately 1 Å) and therefore capable of providing very high resolving power. Physicists and chemists have known for decades that x-rays will reflect from planes of regularly arranged atoms in a crystal in a manner formally like the reflection of light from surfaces. Similarly any biological substance with large arrays of repeating identical subunits will, under proper conditions, reflect x-rays in complicated patterns which can be used to deduce the arrangement of these regular subunits. This subject is far beyond us here, since the results of x-ray diffraction can be interpreted only by extremely complex mathematical analysis. Even the best of modern (1965) computers require months to analyze the results of complicated x-ray patterns. Although this is not as appealing to the beginner as the electron microscope, which shows us a direct picture of the object, x-ray data can be far more revealing of fine details of structure whenever they exist in any repeating pattern. To give a very crude analogy, let us suppose that an elaborate crystal chandelier consisting of many regularly spaced cut-crystals of glass could be observed only through the spots of light reflected from these crystals onto a suitably placed wall. One could, after a good deal of observation, connecting the pattern of spots and the angle of the beam of light relative to the chandelier and wall, begin to understand the arrangement of the components of the chandelier and possibly to deduce the shapes of the individual crystals. But it is perfectly obvious that this is a horrible job compared to looking at a few properly taken direct pictures of the chandelier. So it is with x-rays compared to the electron microscope.

Why use x-rays, then? Because they have a much greater resolving power for atomic "chandeliers," if you will, provided the atomic structures have regularities. And biological objects *do* have regularities. Proteins and viruses can sometimes be crystallized, as we have seen, and these crystals consist of millions of the individual component molecules or viral particles, all arranged identically with respect to their subunits —the amino acids, nucleotides, and so on. Sometimes, even though the material cannot be truly crystallized it can be drawn into a fiber in which long threads or rods are arranged exactly parallel, and hence the regularities are at least observable in two dimensions. In such instances (TMV, DNA) the x-ray can potentially—if one is prepared to invest several years of work with a high-speed computer—tell us exactly where each atom is located with respect to all of the others.

Needless to say, very few viruses have been subjected to this elaborate analysis. One of the very few is TMV—again. The reason is, as usual, basically the ease of preparation and purification. But two other principles are here important. The rodlike structures formed crystals which could be oriented for x-ray studies, and the form was so simple and distinctive that it lent itself readily (if you want to consider several years of work by very talented people as "readily") to interpretation. Largely through the work of Rosalind Franklin, a most attractive and brilliant woman who died tragically of cancer just as the TMV structure was completed, we now know a great deal about the exact arrangement of the component parts of this virus. The x-ray work, combined with the electron microscope studies, has told us that the virus is composed of thousands of protein subunits stacked like lighthouse steps holding a strand of RNA in this helical form * (Figure 6·7). We even have a pretty good idea of the arrangement of the amino acids in the individual subunits through a combination of the x-ray results with biochemical analyses of the sequences. This is truly a fabulous achievement. It closely approaches the last link in the chain of antivitalism. TMV is a

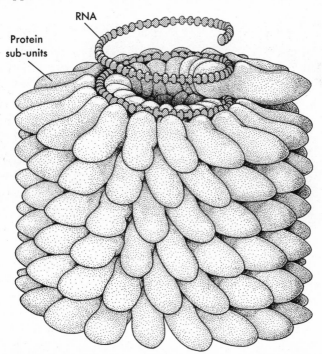

RNA

Protein
sub-units

Figure 6·7. The arrangement of protein sub-units and the RNA of tobacco mosaic virus. [From Dr. D. L. D. Caspar, Children's Cancer Research Foundation, Boston, Massachusetts.]

---

* An ordinary steel spring is a helix. A "spiral staircase" is usually really helical.

biological object capable of reproduction, having genetic properties, known to cause disease to plants and economic damage to the extent of millions of dollars. We can now describe it almost completely in terms of known arrangements of atoms of carbon, hydrogen, oxygen, nitrogen, sulfur, and phosphorus. As soon as we know the ribonucleic acid sequence—another fantastically difficult but possible job—the description will be complete. I suspect that this goal may be realized before the first freshman readers of this book obtain their Ph.D. degrees.

The Detailed Structure of Viruses

Although no other virus is known as well as TMV, we now can describe through combinations, mainly of x-ray analysis and electron microscopy, the basic details of structure of a number of viruses. And the exciting thing is that the viruses turn out to be built on quite simple basic patterns. The protein outside coat, far from being a "bag," is a beautifully constructed geometrical figure (Figure 6·8) made by the putting together of identical subunits of protein into structures many

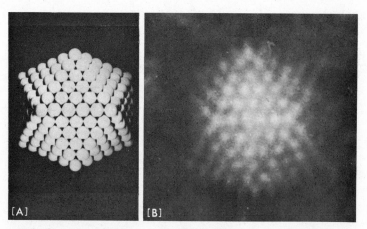

Figure 6·8. Capsomeric structure of adeno virus. A: A model made of plastic balls. B: An electron micrograph of phosphotungstic acid negatively stained virus (× approx. 560,000!) [Photos supplied by Dr. R. W. Horne, Agricultural Research Council, Cambridge, England. From *Advances in Virus Research*, New York: Academic Press, 1963, p. 126.]

of which are like the architecturally famous geodesic domes of Buckminster Fuller. This occurs by no coincidence. Both the dome and virus are constructed for economy and efficiency—simple subunits arranged in the simplest way for maximum capacity and strength. From the point of view of the molecular biologist this is ideal, since it tells us that the ultimate task of the complete definition of living material is conceptually simple. These concepts have been formalized largely on the basis of some suggestions of Crick and Watson concerning the fundamental structure of viruses.

The simple viral particle—now often called a *virion*—consists of a nucleic acid core of genetic material enclosed in and protected by a protein coat (*capsid*). This coat consists of identical protein *structural subunits* of the order of magnitude, perhaps, of 20,000 daltons (molecular weight units) each. The essence of the theory is that the number of the fundamental protein structural units must be a multiple of 60 and that small numbers of these units are combined to form the *morphological subunits* or *capsomers*. The morphological subunits are the balls, wedges, cylinders, or prisms, which can be seen in the electron microscope as the visible elements of viral structure. These units are arranged in one of a very few possible geometric forms. The simplest is the helix, as in TMV. The more general structure is a regular twenty-sided geometric form, the icosahedron, in which each morphological subunit is essentially identical with all others. In fact the final structure is to be considered as though a two-dimentional crystal array has been folded to give a hollow shell. The rules governing the folding provide for maximum economy of surface in relation to space enclosed with the least distortion of the joining of the subunits. Two x-ray crystallographers, D. Caspar and A. Klug, have theorized that basic structural considerations limit the possible numbers of morphological subunits to certain values. One series runs 12, 42, 92, 162, 252 . . . and the other 32, 122, 272. . . . Most viruses seem to fall into the first class. A typical model of this kind of construction, and an actual electron micrograph are shown in Figure 6·8. It should be noticed that the subunits are not *identically* located: most of them are surrounded by six others, but those at the corners of the icosahedron have five neighbors. Recent work shows that the protein subunits of the vertices of adenovirus are both serologically and morphologically different from the rest. The numbers of morphologically recognizable subunits have been observed to vary from the smallest possible number of 12 (found with ϕX-174 phage) to very large numbers, for example, the 812 of the *Tipula iridescent* virus. The crystallographers are sufficiently convinced by the agreement with theory of the structures that have been well established to suggest to the nonconformists that they go back and take more pictures.

More complicated viruses, like influenza or herpes, can assume an outer envelope and/or have a coiled inner nucleoprotein core of helical structure surrounded by an icosahedral capsid. The bacterial viruses, as we know, are often of complex morphology with an icosahedral head and a tail of helical construction.

As this book is being written, the capsomeric structure of only a few viruses has been completely settled. Many are in various stages of analysis, and within a few years we should know the fundamental architecture of all of the important ones.

The Morphology of Nucleic Acid

Our knowledge of the structure of nucleic acid of viruses has advanced enormously in the past decade. The detailed structure of DNA and RNA is becoming known through a combination of studies by a wide variety of physical methods and studies of biological, biochemical, biophysical, and genetic properties. In general we can say that (1) all plant viruses have single-stranded RNA, (2) animal viruses so far can have either single- or (rarely) double-stranded RNA or double-stranded DNA, (3) bacterial viruses so far contain mostly double-stranded DNA but can also have single-stranded DNA or RNA, (4) insect viruses are less studied although most contain RNA and at least one has DNA. Since some of these findings are of recent date, I would not bet much against further permutations.

The most entertaining morphological characteristic of the nucleic acids is their enormous length-to-width ratio. The DNA of T2, for example, has been studied by many methods. The width has been known for some time to be 20 Å as measured both by x-ray analysis and from the electron microscope pictures obtained by Robley Williams and me. The length has been the subject of the most vigorous controversy. Early measurements were badly in error because, it is now known, purified T2 DNA cannot even be pipetted or vigorously shaken without breakage. But the whole molecules were so long that their properties were beyond the known range of the usual physical measurements. By most painstaking and ingenious pioneering methods which required several years to develop, A. D. Hershey solved the problem. Using a carefully controlled high-speed stirrer he was able to break the DNA strands in half. Higher speeds of stirring made quarters. Sedimentation of these molecules showed that previous estimates of the size of T2 DNA had been seriously wrong. The correct size was then determined by radioautography. Radioactive T2 DNA of known specific activity was exposed to a photographic emulsion, and the number of tracks produced per particle (as a result of radioactive decay) was taken as a measure of the DNA size. This showed that the T2 DNA was a single piece of molecular weight 130–135 million daltons. Since we know the density of the DNA we can now calculate the length to be some 63 microns (versus a width of 20 Å or 2 *milli*microns). To give a rough idea of the appearance of such a molecule we may compare it to a line of automobiles bumper to bumper. If each car is 6 feet wide, the line would be 37 miles long and would contain about 12,000 cars.

A remarkable confirmation of these results of physical measurements was obtained through some beautiful electron micrographs taken by A. Kleinschmidt. By osmotically shocking T2 onto the surface of water, he was able to prepare monomolecular films containing DNA. The spread-out molecules were picked up on an electron microscope grid and photographed (Figure 6·9). By painstaking actual measurement of such photographs he found a length of 47 microns, which, considering the nature of the techniques, was in good agreement with the 63 predicted. We should again emphasize, however, that the indirect physical measurements gave the result first. The elegant direct visualization serves largely as confirmation.

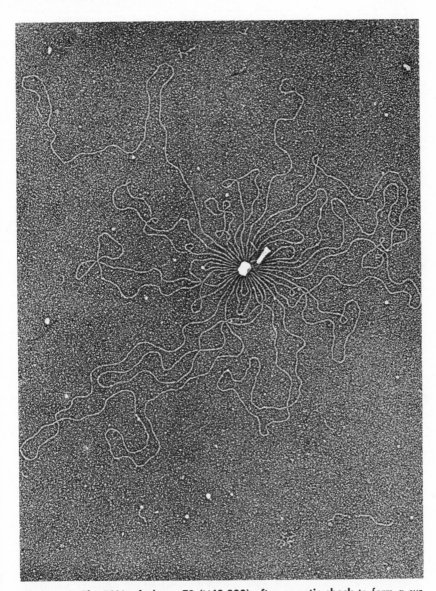

Figure 6·9. The DNA of phage T2 (×48,000) after osmotic shock to form a surface film and rotary shadowing with platinum-palladium. [Photo supplied by Dr. A. K. Kleinschmidt, Virus Laboratory, University of California, Berkeley, Calif.]

The Combined Protein–Nucleic Acid Virion

A point that should be stressed is that although we understand, at least in principle, the construction of the protein coat of viruses and the morphology of DNA, we are still woefully ignorant of the interrelationship of these components. The RNA of TMV seems simply arranged. It is held by the identical protein subunits in the form of a helix (Figure 6·8). Does the nucleic acid dictate the arrangement of the protein? Apparently not, in this instance at least, since we know that if the protein of TMV is purified and then allowed to polymerize, under proper conditions of salt concentration and pH, it will form rods seemingly identical in appearance with those of TMV, with two exceptions —the protein subunits are joined somewhat differently and do not know where to stop; the rods turn out to be of random length. One might postulate that the RNA offers a local heterogeneous environment of pH correct for polymerization in a milieu otherwise unsuitable. Thus the protein may polymerize on the RNA and stop once it reaches the end. This, however, is only a notion.

With the polyhedral viruses we have no idea of the disposition of the nucleic acid except for preliminary data obtained by studies of optical properties which suggest that in some of the bacterial viruses the DNA is arranged in parallel strands. Is the nucleic acid necessary for the assembly of icosahedral capsids? Some of the simple plant viruses (for example, turnip yellow mosaic) can like TMV produce, in the plant, empty protein coats. Whether these once contained nucleic acid we cannot say. Are there in the more complex viruses (influenza or T2), special sites on the nucleic acid that determine its folding and others that are designated as points of protein attachment? These questions should be answered soon, and it is likely that optical methods such as x-ray and the electron microscope will make a major contribution.

Other Optical Methods

I have discussed the electron microscope at length because it is important, but also because it provides a direct image which can be understood by anyone. We have seen, however, that x-ray crystallographic techniques are equally important but tell us something *only* because of theoretical interpretation. It is difficult for the tyro to understand that we learn many of our most important facts from such indirect probes as x-ray diffraction diagrams. With TMV the important rodlike structure was deduced first from observation of birefringence of flow and from the behavior of the virus in the ultracentrifuge, and from its diffusion and viscosity—all observations requiring highly sophisticated interpretation. Light scattering is another important physical property, as are optical dichroism and rotatory dispersion. Unfortunately their determination involves considerable technical difficulties, and the complex theoretical interpretations are far beyond our scope.

Electromagnetic radiation can be used in a quite different way. One might ask, "But what really *happens* when a light beam or an electron or an x-ray hits a virus?" The exact nature of the interaction, and hence alteration or destruction, is a function of the wavelength, which determines the energy, according to Planck's law. Without being mathematical, one can understand intuitively that to be effective the energy of the force must be matched, so to say, with the object involved. A baseball bat can send a baseball into the bleachers, but it has little effect on a thistledown, far less on the air molecules through which it passes. Ultraviolet light can interact destructively with many molecules and thus can inactivate viruses. The particular wavelength that is most effective is exactly that which is absorbed best by the components of nucleic acid, a fact that was the earliest clue to the primary importance of this component of viruses. When the *rate* of inactivation of a virus by radiation is studied, it is found that the virus may be destroyed with *one hit kinetics*. Detailed discussion of this would require application of calculus, but a most important implication is that with a given dose of irradiation the amount of killing of viruses of various sizes will be in proportion to the actual size of the essential genetic material of the virus. With x-rays and other forms of hard irradiation—such as the products of particle accelerators and gamma rays—it has been possible to estimate the size of the essential material of a virus (and this turns out to be the nucleic acid) quite accurately by simply measuring the rate of killing with increasing dosage of irradiation. The beauty of this quite indirect measurement is that it can be done on even a small amount of virus in a quite impure state, in fact even on viral particles as they are being formed in a cell. Such measurements, which were made in the early days of modern virology, turned out to be astonishingly accurate when they were corroborated years later by the tedious procedures of actually purifying and measuring the size of the nucleic acid by other methods. These studies of the interactions of radiation with viruses are again a demonstration of the great power of even simple physical measurements backed up with sound theoretical interpretation.

Hydrodynamic and Thermodynamic Methods

This fearsome title covers a wide variety of techniques, some of which we shall not even discuss, but several of which have been of great importance in virology. The *ultracentrifuge* we have already considered as a means of purifying viruses. But it can also be used as a very powerful tool for studying important properties. By means of a centrifuge considerably more complicated than the preparative machine, but also designed by Pickels in its modern commercial form, it is possible to accomplish the rather incredible feat of observing the behavior of a suspension of viruses (or other large molecules) while they are being subjected to a centrifugal force in a rotor whirling at speeds up to 60,000 rpm (260,000 times gravity). By means of these observations it is possible to learn quite important things.

We can tell if a virus is homogeneous—that is, if it is uncontaminated by other particles that differ in size. The ultracentrifuge can provide important information about the size of the virus. There are theoretical equations which relate the rate of sedimentation to the particle weight. Unfortunately these are only rigorously applicable through measurement also of the diffusion rate and density of the material. For many practical purposes, however, with particles of similar shape and density, the sedimentation constant affords a direct comparison of viral particle weight on a relative basis. (This is often, somewhat carelessly, called the *molecular weight* of the virus. One would hesitate today in calling even a simple virus a molecule, however. I hesitated in doing so in the first chapter.)

Electrophoresis is another technique that is very useful in characterizing viruses. It is based on the fact that many large molecules and particles of biological interest are electrically charged. This is because they are made up of proteins, some of whose amino acids are acidic and some basic, and of nucleic acid, which is highly charged because of its content of phosphoric acid and of nucleotide bases. If such a charged molecule in solution or suspension in a suitable solvent, such as buffered water with a reasonable content of salt, is subjected to an electric field, the charged molecule will move (migrate) toward either the positive or negative pole. The rate of movement will depend mainly on the charge and the strength of the electric field. The method is fraught with complexities, but it has been extremely useful because it provided a criterion of molecular homogeneity based on properties altogether different from those examined in the ultracentrifuge or electron microscope.

Summary

We have seen that viruses at their simplest consist of nucleic acid and protein, with the protein wrapped around the nucleic acid. Although viruses can take any of several forms, it seems that these are all variants of two basic structures. In one the virus is rod-shaped, and we believe that the nucleic acid is wrapped in subunits of protein arranged in a helical pattern. In the other basic form the virus' outer shell is polyhedral and consists of identical subunits packed together as though a two-dimensional crystalline array had been folded to form a three-dimensional icosahedral shell in which the nucleic acid is contained. Some of the larger viruses are much more complicated. The larger bacterial viruses, for example, T2, have many proteins in their outer coat—some eight or ten are morphologically discernible—with different functions.

A: Albert B. Sabin. **B:** John F. Enders. **C:** Wendell M. Stanley. **D:** E. G. Pickels.
E: Robley C. Williams. **F:** Max Delbrück. **G:** A. D. Hershey. **H:** James D. Watson.
I: Seymour Benzer.

7

The Life Cycle of Viruses

MANY EXPERIMENTS have been done to try to persuade viruses to multiply outside of cells; they have all failed so far. In general we now know why, as we shall see later. Spiegelman has reported *in vitro* reproduction of a viral RNA, and it is not at all inconceivable that we can cause a complete virus to multiply in a cell-free system in the near future. But the circumstances will be artificial, quite unlike any that exist in the present nonlaboratory world. For the purposes of the present discussion we can say that viruses, as biological objects, are obligate parasites and must multiply in a cell.

The General Life Cycle

The fact that viruses have a real life cycle was suspected for a number of years before it was definitely shown to be true by Max Delbrück with the bacteriophage. Delbrück was a nuclear physicist, working in Bohr's laboratory, and first heard about the bacteriophage at a seminar in Bohr's home. He became extremely interested in this strange tiny object with the amazing ability to reproduce itself a hundredfold in about a third of an hour in a simple cell under controlled conditions. It seemed to him that this was an ideal system with which one could ask and answer straightforward questions about the essential nature of reproduction. Perhaps the most important aspect of his approach to the phage is revealed in his decision to begin with the most basic fact possible—demonstration that it has a reproductive cycle and is therefore living—and to work from there asking one question at a time and building each new experiment on the already established facts. This was a brilliant approach in any case and particularly so with the bacteriophages, because up to that time so much misinformation and "soft" information was mixed with the facts that no one knew what to trust.

Delbrück devised—or perhaps one should say perfected, since somewhat similar experiments had been done by others—the *single step growth* experiment. He mixed phages with cells and allowed them to interact for, say, five minutes. *The mixture was then greatly diluted.* He knew that infection required the collision of a phage with a cell and that if the mixture were greatly diluted almost no collisions would occur and therefore no further infection of cells. This clever trick meant that he could start the life cycle at a definite time—the time of the initial mixing—and could restrict the phage to a *single cycle* of reproduction, since any phage released upon lysis of the diluted infected host cells would not find further cells to attack.

As we can see from Figure 7·1 the cycle consists of several parts. There is an initial phase (*latent period*), during which the infected cells seem to do nothing; the number of plaque-forming units (PFU)

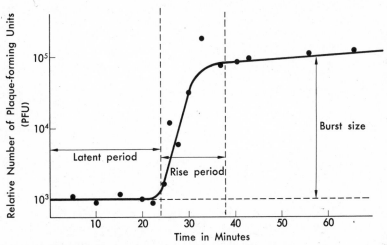

Figure 7·1. Representation of a single step growth experiment, showing the life cycle of a typical phage as T2.

remains quite constant. Then, at a time that is characteristic for each phage and set of conditions, a sudden rise of some hundredfold occurs in the number of PFU. After this brief *rise period,* the number remains quite constant; the reproductive cycle has been terminated by the lysis (bursting) of the infected cell. The ratio of final to input phage is called the *burst size* and is also characteristic.

We have, then, defined the life cycle of the bacterial virus. It was a long time before the life cycle of any other sort of virus was similarly described. In recent years, however, it has been possible to do rather parallel experiments with animal cells in tissue culture, and the general results are similar with some exceptions, which we shall consider as we go along. But what happens during the various stages? Obviously many questions have been raised, and we shall try to answer as many of them as possible.

How Viruses Get to Cells

With most viruses we still have little opportunity to ask how they get to the host cell. Some plant viruses, for example, must be rubbed on a leaf, as TMV. They presumably enter a damaged cell and go heaven knows where in the complex structure of the leaf. Others must be introduced by an insect, perhaps into some quite specific place or type of cell, but we have little knowledge of this nor conviction that the cell that is first entered is the one in which the virus multiplies. Animal viruses in the intact animal offer us, if anything, fewer clues. How the virus enters, where it goes, and how, are almost totally mysterious except in the most general terms. In tissue culture we have a considerably better opportunity to study the process, but this method of cultivation came late in the game.

One of the early experiments with phages was concerned with the encounter between the virus and the cell. We shall discuss this in a little detail, since it is an excellent illustration of the potentiality of the system to provide a concrete answer to a very direct question, "Do bacteriophages attach to the host cell?" The reason that it was possible to answer this question definitively is that it is easy to separate host cells, either infected or not, from the viral particles by simply centrifuging the mixture in an ordinary laboratory (or so-called clinical) centrifuge. The cells, being large, sediment rapidly and completely in a few minutes; the much smaller viruses do not sediment at all under these conditions. We mix phages and suitable cells and at various times remove samples and centrifuge them. We can then assay the supernatant fluid for viruses and demonstrate that as time goes on before centrifuging, fewer and fewer particles are found. It is possible to show that the missing viruses can be accounted for in terms of infected cells; the assays of the supernatant and pellet (if cells were in excess) add up to the original input virus. The rate at which phages attach to cells can be described exactly by a very simple mathematical expression.

Now that we know that they attach to cells, we might ask how they get there. As I have already commented, this point was considerably obscured by the electron microscope pictures which showed that most bacteriophages have tails. Obviously they swim to the host cell. Alas, the obvious is not always the truth. A lot of hard work and the use of rather elaborate equipment were necessary to show definitely that the viruses do not swim, but arrive at the cell only by processes of random collision caused mostly by Brownian motion. Brownian motion is the movement of microscopic or submicroscopic particles caused by collision with the moving molecules of the gas or liquid in which they are suspended.

Having arrived at the cell surface, what happens next? Obviously they must attach. How? A series of simple but ingenious experiments by T. T. Puck showed that the primary attachment is by means of ionic bonds. That is to say that certain negative charges on the cell surface attract certain structures containing positive charges on the virus, and vice versa. It is believed that a pattern of such charges exists on the cell and a complementary pattern exists in all viruses that can attach. Puck also was able to make a number of statements about the kinds of particular molecular groupings that are probably involved.

We have now gotten the bacteriophage to the cell, and we are quite certain that we understand the mechanism. With animal viruses the available information suggests that the process so far is quite similar; with plant viruses we know almost nothing.

We might ask further just where the specific attachment site of the virus is located. When it was assumed that the bacterial virus swam with its tail, it seemed obvious that it arrived at the cell head first and chewed its way in; the early electron micrographs seemed to confirm this since they showed phages nicely packed around cells head first. Alack! Only after several years of such belief by virologists, Tom Anderson was able to show by a special technique that on the contrary the phage attaches tail first (Figure 7·2). The writer, always a diehard, and R. C. Williams set out to disprove this obviously nonsensical observation, and after confirming it and eating suitable amounts of crow,

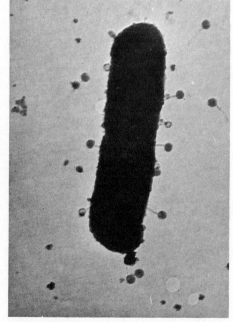

Figure 7·2. Electron micrograph of phage T5 attached to E. coli (×39,000). [From T. F. Anderson, *Cold Spring Harbor Symposia, 18:* 199, 1953.]

showed further that the tails of the large phages (T2) have attached to them long fibers which seem to act as tentacles in seeking out the cell surface. The flailing fibers (Brownian motion) hit the cell many times each time a virus passes near and hence can seek out the complementary pattern of charges for adsorption. In this way virtually every "collision" (as calculated by mathematical theory) can be successful even though the virus must find a particular spot. The animal and plant viruses have no tails, but several animal viruses (adeno and influenza) have projecting spikes which presumably serve a similar purpose.

There are hundreds of *receptors* for every virus on every cell. We might also ask where they are located. The late Wolf Weidel showed that they seem to lie in the various interwoven layers of the surface of *E. coli*—the host for T2 phages—and that their complex chemical construction consists of enormous molecules of lipoprotein or lipopolysaccharide.

The Latent Period—Intracellular Phage

The major mystery of the single step growth cycle was what the phages were doing during the latent period. Nothing could be seen to be happening insofar as the number of plaques remained constant, but surely all sorts of entertaining things must be going on somewhere, probably inside the cell. Getting into the cell, however, was a very tricky matter. Were the phages being formed gradually inside the cell, or were they really formed instantaneously at the moment of release? Were they inside the cell at all? At least one well-known scientist believed that lysis occurred at the outset and that the phage grew by picnicking on the debris.

These questions were answered by some very pretty experiments of A. H. Doermann, who discovered two ways of breaking open the infected cells. Both methods gave the same astonishing result; immediately after the infection the original phage disappears, and no new particle can be found until some 13 minutes later (with phage T2). What had happened to the infecting phages? They were not detectable outside the cell; they were not to be found inside. The new crop of particles appeared inside the cell, suggesting clearly that this was where the reproduction had occurred, but how could the cell make duplicates of a particle that was not there? Doermann suggested, among several possibilities, that the phages had gone into some undetectable form. This answer is correct, but in a way that was really undreamed of, and the solution of the enigma of the *eclipse period* (the period when no virus can be found in the cell) came only some years later. The solution came through an experiment, or set of experiments, that revolutionized biology.

The Hershey-Chase Experiment

Even though the Hershey-Chase experiment is biochemical in nature, and for that reason might more properly be described in the next chapter, it is so fundamental to understanding the life cycle of the virus that we shall anticipate somewhat and consider it here. As background, we should list several important facts known to A. D. Hershey that prompted him to do this set of experiments. (1) Phage T2, like all viruses, consists of nucleic acid and protein. It had been shown that if the virus is osmotically shocked by sudden dilution from a solution high in salt to one very low, the nucleic acid separates from the protein. If the results of this process are observed in the electron microscope, it can be seen that the protein part consists of particles that look for all the world like ordinary phage except that they now lie quite flat on the microscope grid and their heads are no longer opaque to the electron beam. In short they look like a ghost of the phage and are so called. The DNA can also be seen as gobs of material mostly in enormously extended strand form (Figure 6·9). These observations showed that the DNA lives inside the protein bag of the head and that it is not very firmly attached; in fact it seems all too anxious to get out if given a chance. (2) We have already seen that phages attach to the cell by their tails. Shortly thereafter, it can be seen in the electron microscope that the heads of the phages are now empty (Figure 7·2). (3) The Waring blender—exactly the same machine used to make up frozen orange juice for your breakfast—will prevent the infection of cells by phages when the mixture is violently stirred by its high-speed blade. These observations were known to everyone in the phage field, and when they are presented in this way the next step seems obvious by hindsight. But it took Hershey to isolate these facts from the thousands of others and to think of the beautiful set of experiments that are now widely known as "the Hershey-Chase experiment."

Proteins are made up of amino acids, which, in turn, are constructed of atoms of carbon, hydrogen, oxygen, nitrogen, and sulfur. Nucleic acids are made up of the first four kinds of atoms plus phosphorus. If one wants, then, to answer the question of where the protein goes during phage infection and where the nucleic acid goes, this can be done by labeling the phage with radioactive sulfur, as a protein marker, or phosphorus, as a nucleic acid marker. It is often said that in science the most important part of making a discovery is the formulation of the proper question. We have here clearly a magnificent demonstration of this truism. Hershey and Chase labeled the protein of T2 phage with sulfur. They demonstrated that when phages are adsorbed to cells or cell wall fragments the sulfur in the protein ghost remains attached to the bacterial cell walls. The phosphorus-labeled DNA, on the contrary, becomes associated with the material inside the cell (Figure 7·3). Since it had been clearly established that the phages multiply inside the cell, and since the protein never got in, this suggested that the part of the T2 phage that is responsible for the reproductive processes is the DNA. You may object on the basis that the protein was, after all, attached to the cell and could possibly play a very important role even from the outside. Hershey answered this objection by a remarkable sort of encore to the main experiment. He demonstrated that if the newly infected cells are violently agitated in the Waring blender, the sulfur-

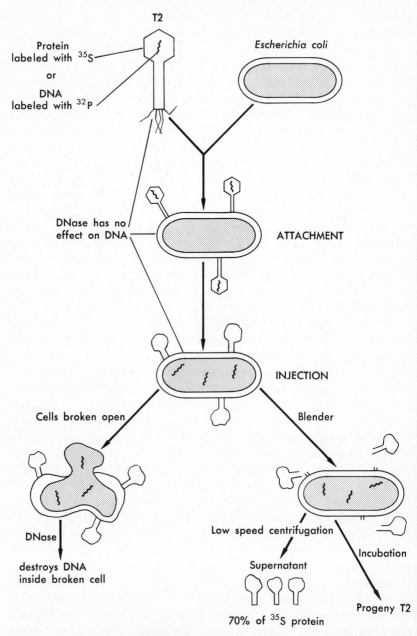

Figure 7·3. Schematic representation of the Hershey-Chase experiment. The DNA of the infecting phage becomes associated with intracellular material; the protein remains almost entirely outside the cell and can be removed with little effect on the processes of phage reproduction. The phages and cells are not drawn to scale.

labeled protein can be sheared off from the cells to a very considerable degree, *without appreciable reduction of the ability of the cells to produce phage particles.* Little of the phosphorus (the nucleic acid) is lost in this process. The inference, then, is that *phage replication is under the direction of the nucleic acid* and that the protein plays no informational role in heredity.

Actually, the foregoing conclusion was reinforced by further experiments in Hershey's remarkable paper. We have somewhat oversimplified the results, but the essence of it, as shown by enormous amounts of confirmatory work since, is as just described. We are now similarly sure that DNA is the molecular repository of genetic information in all higher organisms. It is no exaggeration to say that this discovery revolutionized biology. Previously it had been assumed by nearly all biologists that the protein played a most important, if not key, role. It might be noted, ironically, that this discovery was not really new; a number of years before it had been shown that heritable properties could be conferred on pneumococcal bacteria by purified DNA from other pneumococci with different properties. But bacteria were then regarded as kooky organisms anyway. They were thought by most bacteriologists to have no nuclei, and this phenomenon of *transformation* was considered to be some sort of oddball triggering or something. By the time of the Hershey-Chase experiment, however, so much was known about the life cycle of phages that no such trivial interpretation was possible; it was largely a matter of providing the necessary information at the necessary time—the time when people were prepared to believe it.

To point up the importance of this discovery, we might note that seven Nobel Prizes in biology have since been awarded for work based on the genetic importance of nucleic acid. We shall see more prizes in this area before we are finished with it. The field of molecular biology really came into flower with the idea that all genetic phenomena are interpretable in terms of the definable structure of the nucleic acids.

Invasion

We now know the reason for the surprising discovery of Doermann that no virus is found in the cell during early infection. With the protein left outside the cell, the nucleic acid displays no infectivity by the usual assays. The processes by which the nucleic acid, by providing new genetic information, takes over the cell metabolism for viral reproduction will be considered in the next chapter. We also know that the detailed mechanism by which T2 DNA enters and subverts a cell is unusual, if not unique to T2, T4, and T6. In general, however, all virulent viruses commandeer a cell to some degree. This process is described as *invasion.*

How does the DNA enter the cell? The tail fibers of T2 are responsible for attachment, as we have already said. The remainder of the tail seems to be a contractile sheath which, possibly acting much like a muscle, drives a central core, or pin, into the cell. Enzyme action on the cell wall is also involved in this process, perhaps to soften the wall or to strip it away altogether. Then some sort of a plug is removed (enzyme action again?) from the tail end, and the DNA goes into the cell through the central channel which has been seen in the core. The process seems superficially so akin to the action of a hypodermic syringe that it is called *injection*. I object to this facile analogy largely because it is so facile. It might be pointed out that the head does *not* completely collapse during the process: the DNA is not literally squeezed out like toothpaste. The molecular interpretation is unknown, but under study.

But what about the parallel processes in nontailed viruses—as virtually all animal and plant viruses? It is clear from electron microscopic study of sections of animal-virus-infected tissue culture cells that the mechanism here is rather different. The viruses probably attach to the cells through electrostatic forces as with phages. With influenza and some related viruses there seem to be attachment spikes, and the second step involves action of a viral enzyme on the cell. But the invasion is mediated by the cell itself through processes known as phagocytosis or pinocytosis. One of the properties of many animal cells is the ability to take up foreign material, food for example, by these mechanisms, and viruses seem to be able to fool the cell into taking them up similarly. Thus the cell invaginates (creates an internal pocket), surrounding the particle. The pocket seals off from the outside and disintegrates, leaving the virus inside the cell (Figure 7·4). Subsequently the viral pro-

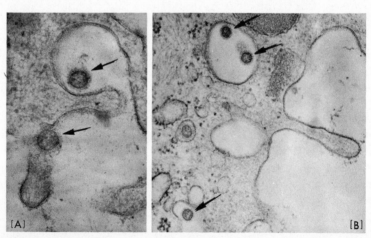

Figure 7·4. Influenza virus particles (arrows) in A are in the process of being phagocytized—taken up into a pocket being formed at the cell surface. In B the pocket has sealed off, leaving the viruses in a vesicle within the cell. [Photos supplied by Dr. Samuel Dales, Rockefeller Institute, New York. From *Virology*, New York: Academic Press, 1962, p. 489; and *Progress in Medical Virology*, Basal/New York: S. Karger.]

tein is apparently attacked by enzymes (from cellular lysozomes?), and the nucleic acid is released. The end result, then, is the same as with T2. Invasion is less understood with plant viruses, but it seems clear that the virus is deposited in the plant by processes involving cellular damage and is then, as with the animal viruses, uncoated.

Morphological Changes—Viral Assembly and Release

So far as the cell is concerned, the processes of invasion cause little metabolic disturbance; if the total respiration of bacterial cells is studied, no change is found at all. This important observation by S. S. Cohen was one of the first clues to the fact that the virus alters the cell metabolism as little as possible (Chapter 8). In the bacterial cells, the virulent viruses, as T2, very quickly disrupt the entire genetic apparatus of the cell, as can be seen in the ordinary microscope or better in the electron microscope. But with some cells, particularly with some of the animal cells, virtually no changes can be observed at first. In plants, viral infection apparently *increases* the energy-producing metabolism.

As we have seen, a time variously called the *dark* or *eclipse period* then ensues during which no viruses can be detected in the cell. Toward the end of this period, just before new, infectious viral particles are detectable, the electron microscope shows a rapid accumulation of objects that, from size and morphology, can be considered as viral precursors. These steps were first studied with the bacterial viruses. We owe the development of many of the very difficult techniques of fixation, sectioning, and staining to E. Kellenberger and his collaborators. They were able to show that a large part of the central portion of the *E. coli* infected by T2 becomes filled with a dense mass of DNA fibrils (Figure 7·5). Then electron opaque areas (*concretions*) of size appropriate to the phage appear. Next are seen clearly discernible phage heads and finally complete particles. All of these seem to accumulate randomly in the cell. Quite parallel processes have been observed in sections of animal-virus-infected tissue culture cells, but here the cells are so much larger that the viral replication can often be localized with respect to various cellular morphological components.

One might suppose naïvely that viral release occurs just because the cell becomes intolerably packed and bursts. A comparison of various viruses and a little arithmetic employing their dimensions and burst sizes show that this cannot be the case. Most phages and some of the animal viruses, for example polio, appear to be released by destruction of the cell. With some of the really small bacterial viruses and several of the animal viruses, however, the particles apparently simply leak out of the cell somehow, causing little or no damage. Several known animal viruses, as influenza, leave the cell by a process of budding morphologically much like the entry process in reverse. The plant viruses are seemingly released only by damage of the cellular structure either

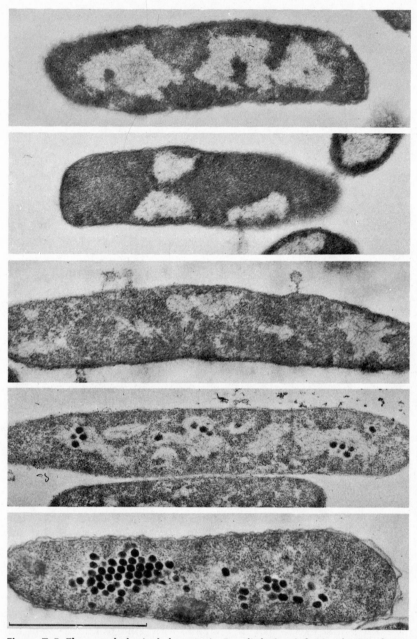

Figure 7·5. The morphological changes in *E. coli* during infection by T2 phage. The successive electron micrographs of sectioned bacteria (× approximately 36,000) show the cell (*from top to bottom*) uninfected and at 4, 8 to 10, 11 to 14, and 30 minutes postinfection. Note the dispersion of the nuclear material of the cell in the second picture, the accumulation of very fine fibrillar material in the third, and the appearance of increasingly phagelike particles in the last two photographs. [Photos supplied by Dr. E. Kellenberger and collaborators, Centre de Microscopie Electronique, University of Geneva, Switzerland.]

through autolysis (the rotting of dead cells), by gross mechanical damage, or by selective damage through insect feeding. One way or another, then, all viruses manage to get back into circulation ready to infect suitable hosts.

Summary

The processes by which viruses reach their host cells are largely mechanical and involve no active role for either the virus or the host. With animal and bacterial viruses, attachment to a cell occurs through low-energy bonds, largely electrostatic. In many instances viral enzymes act on the cell surface. The viral nucleic acid is then released inside the cell. This process of invasion may kill the cell but often results in little gross change. The progeny viruses accumulate, are assembled, and are finally released by various processes, which may or may not result in gross damage to the cell.

8

The Biochemistry of Viral Reproduction

THE DETAILS of the biochemistry of viral reproduction are beyond the scope of this book. The main features of the process, however, are so basic to all of biology that we shall consider the principles involved, the development of the fundamental patterns, and the results, even though we omit most of the actual chemistry.

The Duality of Function of the Viral Particle

When a virus is away from its host cell it has no detectable living function whatsoever. It does not metabolize, for example, it requires no nutrients, no air, and some can survive totally desiccated. It responds to external stimuli only as would any inert particle of similar size, shape, and general molecular constitution. It can be destroyed or even mutated by radiation or certain chemical or physical treatments, but it does not react in any positive way with its surroundings. Such enzymatic properties as it possesses (and these have been detected only for the larger viruses) seem concerned solely with its ability to infect the host cell. Thus such a viral particle can scarcely be considered as living at all; in this state it is commonly referred to as a *resting virus*.

But, when a virus encounters a suitable host, suddenly it takes on the attributes of a living thing. As described in the previous chapter, it reproduces with a well-defined life cycle. In doing so, it institutes changes in the chemistry of its host. It is capable of manifesting genetic properties, such as mutation and recombination. The virus in this living, reproducing form is commonly referred to as *vegetative*. As we have seen, the virus has a protein outer coat. In the process of separating the protein from the nucleic acid the virus is converted from resting to vegetative existence.

The Duality of Function of the Vegetative Virus

As humans we like to think that we exist for very elevated and complex purposes. With most other organisms, particularly viruses, we can see in a fairly uncluttered way that their properties are clearly designed to facilitate survival and reproduction. The forms that these properties take are incredibly diverse and complicated. As is well known, it is nearly impossible to find on the earth a niche to which no organism has adapted.

Viruses, too, have their niche. They must withstand the hard, cruel world as resting particles until they happen on a host cell in which they can multiply. Then they must attach to it, get inside, convert to the vegetative form, persuade the host to stop its normal business or at least modify it, and direct the synthesis of new protein coats for the progeny viruses. All these are specific, genetic properties of viruses and are the result, primarily, of the ability of the virus to dictate the synthesis of a variety of proteins. The actual self-duplication of the nucleic acid genetic material of the virus is referred to as its *autocatalytic* function. The ability to cause the synthesis of specific proteins with properties necessary to the replication, protection, or other functions of the virus has been called its *heterocatalytic* property.

The Autocatalytic Function

The Hershey-Chase experiment made it apparent that the vegetative function of the virus T2 is expressed as replication of its DNA. How can an object reproduce itself?

THE THEORY OF SELF-DUPLICATION.   We can describe reproduction as the process of (1) accumulating a sufficient number of subparts, (2) arranging them, (3) fixing them in the arranged positions so that the result is a duplicate of an original, or parent, object. The provision of the subunits can occur by chance through some external agency, or it may be part of the heterocatalytic function of the reproducing object. We shall consider this problem with respect to viruses below and with respect to the origin of life in the last chapter. The key problem for the present discussion is the arranging of subunits to form a duplicate of the parent object, and no matter how complex the events of reproduction, the parent object itself must contain the pattern of specificity. Consider the simplest possible case. If we have a general object, "a-b-c-d-e-f . . .," it can reproduce if we can attract to each subcomponent "a" another "a," to each "b" another "b," and so on, and then link them up and split the whole array apart from the parent to form a progeny object.

This process, illustrated in Figure 8·1, is reproduction, because it represents creation of a duplicate ordered pattern. But you will notice that we have introduced a peculiar property of each parental subunit. We have said, perforce, that each one will attract to its *back* the *front* of the new (progeny) subunit, or vice versa. That is to say, we have assumed that the back of each one is *complementary* to the front.* We could, of course, assume that the subunits are matched front to front. But if we do, the array produced is not a duplicate of "a-b-c-d-e-f . . ." but a mirror image or complement of it, as shown also in Figure 8·1. If such a complement in turn goes through the cycle it will, like any complementary mold, produce duplicates of the parent particle. So the principle of complementarity is introduced again. In fact it is seemingly impossible to devise a general model of reproduction that fails to involve this principle at some step. In making

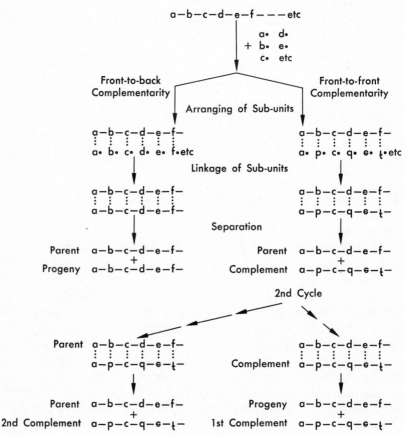

Figure 8·1. Schematized and idealized replication by processes of direct and complementary copying.

duplicates of artifacts of any kind we are very familiar with this way of reproducing things. The type from which this page was printed was a mirror image of the text. The ordinary photographic processes involve

---

* A special case is that in which each unit is quite symmetrical and possesses no back and front, but this restriction seems, so far, irreconcilable with the specificity requisite in any real biological reproducing system. We see this replicative scheme operating in crystal formation.

the use of a negative that is a complement of the original both spacially and with respect to light values. Castings of plaster, bronze, iron, glass, and so on, are made by first forming a complementary mold. This, then, is by far the most usual way of producing replicates of an object.* The theoretical problem of using a complementary intermediate, of course, is that the mold must be constructed and then has no further function once replication is complete. It is a wasteful way of doing things and the selective processes of evolution leave little allowance for waste.

THE WATSON-CRICK DNA AUTOCATALYST. The Hershey-Chase experiment had shown that T2 DNA must be duplicated in the *E. coli* cell. In considering the possible method of replication of DNA, James D. Watson, a young American biologist, and F. H. C. Crick, an English x-ray crystallographer, had the principle of complementarity well in mind. They also had at their disposal several known facts about DNA. (1) The molecule is composed of four different nucleotide subunits. These differ only in that each contains one of four organic bases—adenine, thymine, cytosine, and guanine. (2) These bases can occur in the DNA of various biological species in widely differing proportions, but many painstaking analyses by E. Chargaff had shown certain fixed ratios. The amount of adenine (which we shall usually designate merely as "A") equals the amount of thymine ("T"), and the amount of Guanine ("G") equals the amount of cytosine ("C"). (3) The beautiful x-ray diffraction patterns of DNA obtained by the English crystallographer M. H. F. Wilkins (Figure 8·2) suggested strongly that the molecule is helical in form. (4) The dimensions and density of the helix suggested strongly that it is two-stranded.

It seems clear that Watson and Crick had in mind from the outset a beautifully simple concept. The one-to-one ratio of A to T and G to C suggested that the molecule might have complementarity built in, and the possibility of a two-stranded structure made this look even more attractive. Their problem was to build a model, literally, using plastic balls that could be fitted together and whose proportions and bonding were correct for the various atoms of carbon, hydrogen, nitrogen, oxygen, and phosphorus constituting the component molecules of the DNA. The model had to fit the facts provided by the x-ray work; that is to say, it had to have a three-dimensional arrangement that, on the scale of real DNA, would scatter x-rays exactly to fit the complex pattern shown in the pictures obtained by Wilkins. But by far most important of all, the structure had to be one that could reproduce in a manner consistent with the known facts of physics, physical chemistry, biochemistry, and biology.

That Watson and Crick succeeded is now known to all students of

---

* We might note that it is not the only way. A key-making machine and many office copiers, for example, produce direct duplicates.

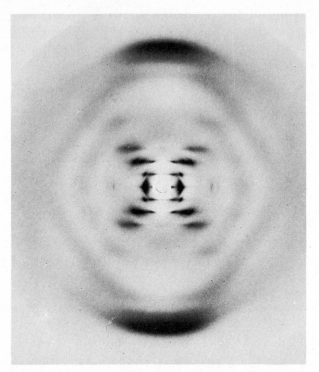

Figure 8·2. X-ray diffraction diagram of DNA obtained by exposure to the x-ray beam of a stretched fiber of DNA in an atmosphere of controlled humidity. Although the exact interpretation involves extremely sophisticated mathematical analysis, it might be noted that the X pattern of spots is typical of helical molecules. [Photo supplied by Dr. M. H. F. Wilkins, Biophysics Research Unit, Kings College, London.]

modern biology and virtually to the well-informed housewife. A real understanding and appreciation of their structure of DNA is possible only with considerable knowledge of organic and physical chemistry, but the essential features necessary to understanding of the biological implications can be fairly simply described. Ordinary DNA consists of two strands of polynucleotides intertwined in a helical pattern, as shown in Figure 8·4. Each strand consists of a backbone of alternating molecules of a sugar, deoxyribose, and phosphate held together by strong chemical bonds (so-called primary bonds). In the final structure the two backbone strands are of opposite polarity, in that the sugar molecule is linked to the phosphate unsymmetrically (as indicated in Figure 8·3). If one strand is considered linked head to foot, the other is identical in backbone structure but reversed. Also linked to each of the deoxyribose molecules by strong bonds and projecting from the backbone is one of the four bases, A, T, G, or C. These bases, however, face *inward* in the duplex structure and are arranged on the two strands in a completely complementary fashion. Every A on the one strand is paired

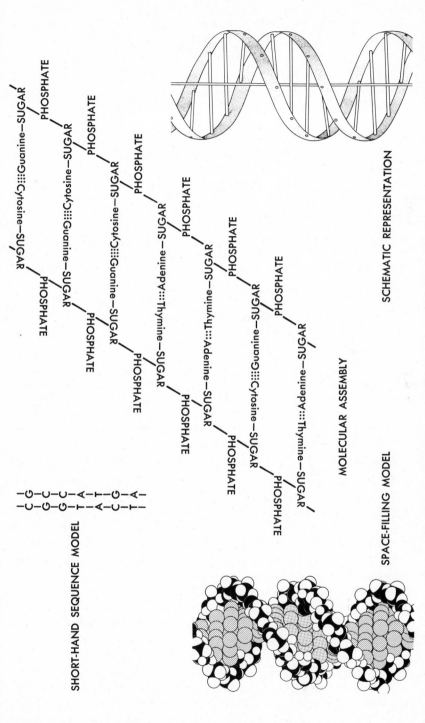

SHORT-HAND SEQUENCE MODEL

MOLECULAR ASSEMBLY

SPACE-FILLING MODEL

SCHEMATIC REPRESENTATION

Figure 8·3. Various representations of two-stranded DNA. Principal features are the complementarity which is built in and the possibility for unfolding and refolding by breaking the comparatively weak hydrogen bonding (dotted bonds) between the strands.

77

with a T on the other, every G with a C. The pairs are matched and held together by specifically located *hydrogen bonds,* which individually are very weak at room or biological temperatures. Since there is a base pair at each step of the duplex helix, however, and since each pair is held together by two (A–T) or three (G–C) of these bonds, the cumulative effect is that of holding the two strands together strongly, as a whole, even though any given pair is readily separated.

It can be seen that a mechanism for reproduction is inherent in this structure. Either by chance, which would occur frequently with these low-energy bonds, or conceivably by the action of a specific enzyme, the two strands might be separated momentarily at one end as indicated in the sequence of drawings of Figure 8·4. But if an appropriate nucleotide—for example, an adenine nucleotide to match the thymine end of one strand—is inserted, the strands are now prevented from going back together at that point. There is, then, ample opportunity for a thymine nucleotide to be inserted opposite the free adenine end. Now there is a strain on the original structure at this end; it is presumably much easier to open the strands further and to insert still more new matching nucleotides. Thus we have fulfilled the second essential of replication—the arranging of new subunits to match or, in this case, complement those of the parent. As these go into place it is assumed that an enzyme links each such insertion to its predecessor, fulfilling the last requirement of replication—the fixing of the subunits in the required arrangement. The result of this zipper-like action is the assembly opposite each strand of its complement; when the process is complete, two molecules of DNA exist, each identical with the parent double helix and each consisting of one parental and one newly made strand.

This is a beautiful picture. Does it exist in reality? As enormous amounts of data have accumulated we have every reason to believe that this structure of DNA as the genetic substance is universal with very few exceptions (notably certain single-stranded viruses—both DNA and RNA), and accounts for the fundamental mechanism of the autocatalytic reproduction of genetic material of every living thing. The prediction that replicated DNA should contain one new (progeny) and one old (parental) strand has been confirmed in several independent ways for a variety of organisms, including viruses, bacteria, and plants. The actual replicating DNA has been visualized both by autoradiography and in the electron microscope, and the process seems to go exactly as predicted. Wilkins, who did the x-ray work, and Watson and Crick, who proposed the DNA structure, received well-deserved Nobel Prizes in 1962.

The details of the mechanism, oddly enough, are not really known yet. Arthur Kornberg discovered an enzyme capable of forming a complement to a single strand of DNA and received a Nobel Prize for his work in 1959. Unfortunately his enzyme works along the backbone only in one direction; it could not copy both strands from the same end

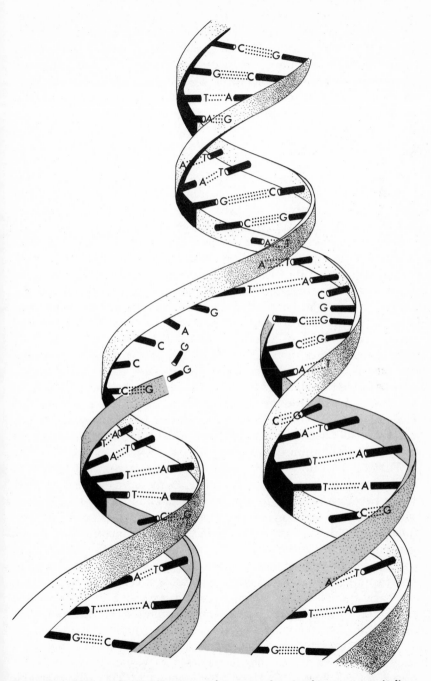

Figure 8·4. DNA replication is assumed to occur by simultaneous unwinding and rewinding of the parent and progeny duplexes. The time required for complete replication of the 190,000 nucleotide-pair T2 DNA is approximately 100 seconds; the rate is, therefore, *1,900 nucleotide pairs per second.*

of the DNA duplex. This particular enzyme is therefore not currently believed to be the long-sought DNA "replicase" but probably a repair enzyme. Kornberg and his collaborators, in a series of monumental papers, nonetheless clearly showed exactly how, biochemically, one can replicate DNA by synthesis of complementary strands; his work is thus of fundamental importance, win, lose, or draw. As the old story goes, the problem of self-replication in biology has been solved in principle, it is now really only a matter of haggling over details.

The Heterocatalytic Function

We seem to have strayed from the virus momentarily, but only because a series of discoveries made with T2 phage led to solution of the problem of self-duplication and turned out immediately to have the most far-reaching implications in all of biology. Now we must return to heterocatalytic function. It is not enough in the present world for a living thing to reproduce its genetic material. It must also, in general, live and function. It must grow, it must provide or acquire the materials needed for self-duplication. It must be equipped to find a biological niche in which it can do these things without undue competition; it must develop ways of eliminating competition or of securing a unique advantage for itself. It must be able to find food and convert it to energy and needed intermediates. As we all know, the result is a most unbelievable complexity of modes of life involving the manufacture, by even relatively simple living forms, of proteins by the hundreds of thousands. Lice, turtle shells, snake venom, squid ink, camel humps, endocrine hormones, luminous organs, webbed feet, marsupial pouches, and warts all have their place in the world, and as biologists we must eventually account for them.

To come back to the virus, on the theory that it may be easier to explain than the mysteries, for example, of the human female, we ask about *its* heterocatalytic functions. At a minimum, as we have seen, viruses seem to need protein coats of specific structure and function. The more elaborate viruses have an intricate composite of external proteins. With T2 the tail constitutes a fascinatingly complicated mechanism for host cell invasion. What else must a virus do? The most obvious thing is that it must parasitize the host cell—must persuade it to make special viral components, both nucleic acid and protein, instead of, or in addition to, performing its normal multifarious functions. How?

PHAGE PARASITISM. Clues to this mystery were sought unsuccessfully for years. In fact the plot thickened as it was found, using the T2 phage–*E. coli* system, that one after another of the cell's functions seemed unchanged by infection. Obviously the major enzymatic pathways of the cell are left to contribute to phage synthesis. This includes those responsible for providing energy and for converting sugar and inorganic compounds to hundreds of small molecules needed for various functions and syntheses. The total cell metabolism is left unchanged, yet in some ways the cell is irretrievably damaged. A bacterium once infected with T2 never divides again. Even bacteria infected with viruses that have been extensively damaged by radiation promptly die.

As discovered by S. S. Cohen, however, important changes occur in the synthesis of macromolecules—proteins and nucleic acids. The over-all production of proteins continues unabated, but, it was shown later, only of those needed for viral reproduction. Those ordinarily present in the cell are made no more. The synthesis of RNA and DNA also stops on infection. Actually, as we shall see a bit later, a very special RNA is made immediately but at a quite low level undetectable in the early experiments. DNA synthesis stops for about eight minutes, one third of the latent period, and then resumes at a rate considerably greater than that which prevailed in the uninfected cell. Cohen later showed that all of this DNA is now phage DNA.

Obviously, it appeared, the cell has been retooled for phage synthesis; only the components needed for T2 DNA and protein are made. But, again, how is the retooling accomplished? How are the usual synthetic processes of the cell blocked?

The answers to these questions were obtained, after several years of work, by a series of discoveries made largely in the laboratories of Cohen and of Kornberg. This work can be described only in chemical terms, but the principles involved are simple. It was found that the DNA of phage T2 is startlingly different from ordinary DNA in that one of the four constituent bases is glucosylated hydroxymethyl cytosine in place of the usual cytosine. New enzymes were discovered which destroy the deoxycytidine phosphate needed for bacterial DNA and make it into the hydroxymethylcytidylic acid needed for T2 but useless to the cell and also into thymidylic acid, which can be used for T2. Furthermore, there is another enzyme which destroys the deoxycytidine triphosphate needed for bacterial DNA syntheses, converting it into more deoxycytidine phosphate to be used in the above two processes. Several more enzymes also appear, all involved in improving the efficiency of the synthesis of DNA components for phages. The essence of the parasitism, then, lies in the rearrangement of nucleic acid metabolism so that it is no longer suitable for making bacterial DNA but only T2 DNA. Since the original DNA (the genetic apparatus) of the cell is destroyed by still another phage-induced enzyme, to which T2 DNA is resistant, and since the original messenger RNA's (discussed later) are very short-lived, the poor cell can make no new cell-directed proteins, far less duplicate its DNA, and is a dead duck indeed.

The important thing to be noted about these changes induced by the invading phage is that they all involve the synthesis of new enzymes—that is, new proteins. How general is this kind of viral parasitism? We do not know yet. But in a number of other virus-host systems, including some involving animal viruses, it is clear that new enzymes are also made, most particularly enzymes apparently designed specifically for the synthesis of nucleic acid intermediates and their polymerization into viral nucleic acid. Viruses have, in other words, two classes of heterocatalytic processes, those designed to aid in parasitism of the host largely by changes in nucleic acid metabolism and those involved in the synthesis of viral structural components. All of these functions involve the making of new proteins. The conclusions must be, then, that the viral DNA in its autocatalytic aspect directs its own replication, in its heterocatylytic function directs largely the synthesis of new proteins.

Information Transfer—The Genetic Code

How general is this? Is the genetic material of all living organisms involved in these functions of heterocatalysis and autocatalysis? All of the information that we have suggests that this is indeed so; genetic properties are expressed (phenotypes created) through the ability of DNA to direct the synthesis of specific macromolecules—structural, enzymatic, and regulatory. How does nucleic acid direct the making of specific proteins? To understand this we must review, in a general way, what we know about proteins and nucleic acids with respect to their potential for specificity—that is to say, their ability to carry information.

During the 1930's, at the beginning of the modern era of biology, it was felt that only proteins, of all known chemical compounds, were sufficiently complicated to allow for all of the nearly infinite variations in biological form and function of the world from virus to whale. The proteins are huge, by molecular standards, with molecular weights in the tens and hundreds of thousands. Each one is composed of an assortment of some 20 amino acid building units. In informational terms we might say that the protein is a language built on 20 letters. The English language is constructed on the basis of 26 letters. Even as the nearly infinite variety of our language derives from permutations of these letters and the words and sentences they compose, so it is with the nearly infinite variety of protein structure.

Consideration of these ideas led to the concept that all biological specificity must lie in huge molecules. Of those known—the proteins, the polysaccharides, and the nucleic acids—none except proteins seemed to have the potentiality for sufficient permutations. A monotony of structure seems characteristic of the polysaccharides, although many of them do possess suspicious immunological specificity. It was believed so for the nucleic acids, which were thought to be composed of identical units of tetranucleotides—that is to say, a completely repeating four-letter-word pattern. Obviously, a monotonous GUAC-GUAC-GUAC-GUAC . . ., for example, would scarcely convey information even to a duck. With the Hershey-Chase experiment, the understanding that bacterial transforming DNA carries information, and the demonstration with several plant and animal viruses that the nucleic acid alone is infectious, came the realization that this could not be so. Even though the genetic nucleic acids are composed, basically, of only four nucleotide building blocks, it *had* to be assumed that these could constitute the letters of a language that was by definition as complex as that of the proteins, since the structure of the proteins must be determined by the information in the nucleic acids. But how is it possible that the two languages can be equivalent?

The answer was first formalized in 1954 by George Gamow, a theoretical physicist, cosmologist, and well-known popularizer of the complexities of science. Obviously one nucleotide cannot be equivalent to one amino acid, but, Gamow suggested, combinations of a small number of nucleotides would serve. His specific suggestion we need not describe, since it turned out to be somewhat incorrect, but his basic idea is exactly right—three successive nucleotide pairs in DNA code for a single amino acid. By invoking the three-to-one ratio it can be seen by anyone familiar with the mathematics of permutations that there are 4^3, or 64, combinations of four different nucleotides taken in groups of three.

But this is more than we need for 20 amino acids. Starting with the idea that nucleic acids had inadequate informational content to account for the requisite permutations of biology, we now have the problem of reducing a 64-letter alphabet of nucleotide triplets to the 20 needed for the amino acids of the protein language. The obvious suggestions are that some of the 64 triplets are *nonsense,* that they correspond to no letter of the protein alphabet, or the alternative that several different nucleotide triplets correspond to the same amino acid, in other words, that the code is *degenerate.* The reasons why we now believe in the triplet code and why we believe that it is degenerate, except for two triplets that are believed to act as message punctuation, would lead us far astray into biochemistry. We shall consider some of the key evidence after we learn something about phage genetics in the next chapter. But we might indulge at this point in a little arithmetic concerned with the information contained in a DNA molecule.

The Informational Content of Viruses

We know that T2 DNA consists of a single molecule of molecular weight about 130 million daltons. This simple statement summarizes the result of nearly ten years of work by some of the most talented people in molecular biology, glosses over some of the liveliest scientific disputes of the current period, and completely omits discussion of the development of whole new areas of physical-chemical research. The fact is now indisputable, however, and has been confirmed by numerous indirect physical measurements using a wide variety of techniques and, finally, by direct measurement of some magnificent electron micrographs (see Figure 6·9) taken by A. K. Kleinschmidt. We also know that the average molecular weight of a single nucleotide pair is about 700. Simple division then tells us that there are about 190,000 nucleotide pairs or 63,000 triplets per T2. If we assume that the average protein consists of combinations of a few subunits (polypeptide chains) of about 200 amino acids each, we can see that T2 could code for 63,000/200, or some 300 such polypeptide chains. Even with the assumption that much of the DNA is concerned with regulation, not direct synthesis of enzymatic or structural proteins, it is still obvious that this virus potentially contains a great deal of heterocatalytic information, much more than enough to account for the, perhaps, 50 proteins that we now believe to be involved in T2 enzymatic parasitism and phage structure. Even the smallest of known viruses has enough potential information for several proteins. For example, the smallest known phage, ϕX-174, has about 1,600 triplets and, on the same basis, could presumably code for some 8 proteins. Toward the other end of the scale, we know that the DNA content of a human cell is about 6×10^{-12} g, or 30,000 times as much as T2. Since human cells are diploid, the relative informational content is really 15,000 fold. Thus if T2 can code for 300 polypeptides, the human cell might contain the information for some 4.5 million. May I again emphasize that we do not know how much genetic material is involved in regulation.

Genetic Material Other than Two-Stranded DNA

Do we really believe in the universal existence of a DNA genetic code and in its heterocatalytic function as the basis for all of the manifestations of life? The answer at present is an emphatic, "Yes," with the only exceptions represented by RNA viruses which seem to shortcut the DNA pattern. The existence of these viruses was known long before the beginnings of molecular biology. All plant viruses seem to contain only RNA, not DNA. For a number of years it was felt that there was no important difference between the two; the sugar of RNA was *ribose,* not the closely related *deoxyribose,* and the base *thymine* of DNA was replaced by a rather similar base, *uracil,* in RNA. With the discovery of the genetic significance of DNA, however, attention was focused also on RNA. Despite many attempts it proved impossible to show a structure for RNA similar to that of the Watson-Crick DNA. That the RNA was nonetheless genetic, in the same sense as the DNA of T2, was, however, shown beyond argument by the remarkable discovery that the RNA of TMV can infect the plant even after the virus has been stripped of its protein. This work, done independently by Fraenkel-Conrat in the United States and by Gierer and Schramm in Germany, was the more puzzling because the RNA of TMV seems clearly to be single-stranded. Many animal viruses are also known to contain single-stranded RNA in place of DNA. It is now established that at least reoviruses (animal cell hosts) and wound tumor virus (plant) have two-stranded RNA.

Several extremely small bacterial viruses turn out to have single-stranded nucleic acid. The related phages S-13 and ϕX-174 contain single-stranded DNA, and the phage f2 has single-stranded RNA. How do these viruses fit into the Watson-Crick picture of self-replication? The answer requires a little more background and will be considered later.

So far as we now know, however, it should be pointed out that we believe that two-stranded DNA is the genetic material of all cellular organisms; as such it has autocatalytic and heterocatalytic functions quite parallel to those observed with T2. We have explained the human female—in principle.

Information Transfer

With the conviction that DNA contains the genetic code and that it is expressed in the form of proteins came the obvious questions of how this process occurs. Gamow had envisioned the amino acids fitting into the DNA helix to form a protein, and indeed models suggested that this might be quite feasible. Unfortunately, the fit became more and more procrustean as our ideas of the code developed. You will remember that immediately after infection of *E. coli* by T2, protein synthesis continues, with the new proteins no longer cell-determined but made under direction of the phage DNA. This system seemed ideal for studying the relationship of a DNA message and its expression in proteins.

We have said that RNA synthesis appears to stop after T2 infection, seeming to indicate that this molecule plays no part in the viral replicative process. In this instance, as not infrequently happens in science, the way out of what was increasingly a dilemma came through reexamination of this supposed fact. Larry Astrachan and Elliott Volkin fed the phage-infected bacteria radioactive phosphorus and then looked at the radioactivity of the RNA of the cell. This method, a far more sensitive indication of synthesis than the analytical methods available to Cohen, showed that a small fraction of the RNA was very rapidly being rebuilt. But the exciting discovery of Volkin and Astrachan was that the new RNA was very similar in the ratio of its four bases to the infecting T2 DNA and unlike the DNA of the original bacterial cell. In other words, the infected cell was making an RNA in which every thymine of the phage DNA was matched by a uracil and in which the other three bases—adenine, guanine, and cytosine—matched the amounts in the phage DNA. It was as though the DNA information had been transcribed into RNA, and *transcription* is the name we now give this process.

It seemed at first as though this RNA copy of the genetic DNA was located in small particles called, at that time, microsomes and known to occur in all living cells. These particles were found to consist of RNA and protein and hence were renamed ribosomes. Several disturbing facts were soon found, however. In general the RNA of purified ribosomes did *not* resemble the DNA of their particular cell. In fact the ribosomes are surprisingly similar in cells whose DNA differs markedly in composition. Furthermore, after phage infection no new ribosomes are made. Yet when bacterial cells were exposed very briefly to radioactive amino acids, the new protein, like the new RNA, was found in ribosomes. These apparent contradictions were resolved by a brilliant suggestion of the French scientists François Jacob and Jacques Monod (Nobel laureates, 1965). They assumed that the ribosomes are indeed stable and not rebuilt in the process of protein synthesis, but that a special RNA, called *messenger* RNA, is transcribed from the DNA, attaches itself temporarily to the ribosome, and there directs the synthesis of the protein.

TRANSLATION AND TRANSFER RNA.   Evidence rapidly accrued to support this suggestion but with one further modification. The amino acids of the protein are not assembled directly on the messenger, but are carried there and placed in order by still a third kind of RNA, so-called *soluble* or *adapter* or *transfer* RNA. We now have evidence that there is probably one such RNA for each or nearly each of the 64 DNA nucleotide triplets (*codons*) and that each is additionally specific for a single amino acid; some amino acids have, perhaps, as many as five s-RNA's specific for them, most have two or three.

The preceding series of reactions comprises the Central Dogma of Molecular Biology (if you are a convert, you believe in the use of capital letters). The information of DNA is a code that is transcribed into RNA and then translated into protein (*translated,* after all, because the protein language is quite different, with 20 letters instead of the 4 of the nucleic acid code). A summary of this somewhat oversimplified but still complicated picture of information transfer is presented in Figure 8·5.

As a result of experimental confirmation of these theories, we must now note that the direct heterocatalytic function of DNA is to specify various RNA's—messenger RNA, transfer RNA, and ribosomal RNA. These in turn accomplish the collection and arranging of the amino acids to form proteins. Why all of this complexity? We do not really know yet, but it is obvious that this system, though elaborate, gives a great flexibility to the cell, allows for evolution in the sense of the use of

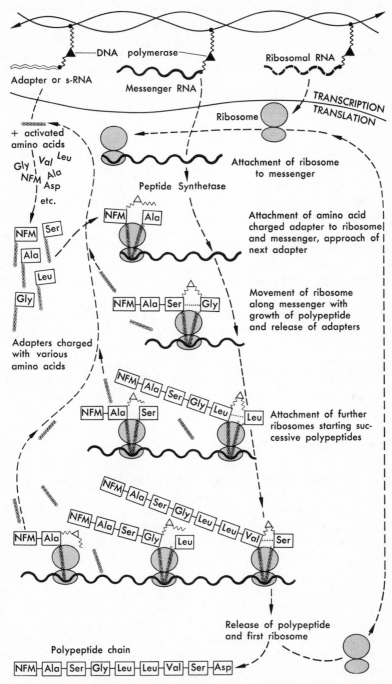

Figure 8·5. Schematized representation of the heterocatalytic activity of DNA —the transfer of genetic information into protein phenotypes. The amino acids are indicated by the standard abbreviations (leu, val, gly, etc.), NFM stands for N-formyl methionine, the initiator for protein translation.

new amino acids, and possibly provides control mechanisms. One end of the transfer RNA recognizes the amino acid; another part recognizes the codon of the messenger. Thus in theory *any* codon could code for *any* amino acid. Is this flexibility actually observed? We do not know for sure yet, but it appears that in a given cell certain of the standard codons are preferred for a given amino acid over certain others. In general the code seems to be invariant and universal in the living forms so far investigated. (These statements may well be out of date, however, by the time you read them.)

THE CODE WORDS. With the realization that DNA must code for protein came many attempts to decipher the genetic code. Doublet codes, triplet codes, overlapping codes, comma-less codes, and so on, were proposed and mostly excluded on one basis or another, frequently because they simply would not account for the amino acid sequences that were beginning to be known in such proteins as insulin and ribonuclease. Although phage and bacterial genetic studies contributed greatly, as we shall see, the breaking of the code came about by the brilliant biochemical experiments of Nirenberg and Matthaei followed by those of Ochoa and of Yanofsky. Tentative assignments for all 64 triplet codons have been made. But to discuss this work would take us far afield from virology. The real point, however, is that research with viruses constantly provided clues, and often key experiments, on which was based this whole amazing set of developments, without doubt among the most important in the history of biology. We shall need to understand these briefly sketched and deliberately oversimplified facts in order to get a picture of molecular genetics, a subject to which study of phages has made the major contribution and which constitutes much of the next chapter.

Summary of the Heterocatalytic and Autocatalytic Functions of T2

We may now relate the preceding picture to viral replication. With T2 and T4, the viruses about which we know the most, we can say with some confidence that the DNA after injection is transcribed into a series of messenger RNA molecules. Interestingly it appears that the transcription occurs by use of the double-stranded molecule but results in single-stranded RNA whose composition is parallel to that of *one* of the DNA strands. The two strands (familiarly known as "Watson" and "Crick") are identical in backbone structure but complementary and reversed in terms of nucleotides and sequences. How the enzyme knows which one to copy is not yet understood, but Sol Spiegelman, who has elucidated many of the key features of the reading of the code, will no doubt have the answer before these words are in print. These new messages attach to the previously made cellular ribosomes, and in turn amino acids are assembled in order by s-RNA molecules (also previously made by the cell) and linked up into new virus-specific, so-called *early* proteins. The enzymes these proteins constitute disrupt the normal cellular nucleic acid metabolism and redirect the cell toward the manufacture of T2 nucleic acid components. The DNA now can exercise its autocatalytic function and begin to replicate itself. At about the same time a series of proteins appears that will constitute the elaborate tail and head structure of T2. Thus all of the component parts of the virus become available. Phage assembly begins, and more and more of these components are made as long as the cell remains intact.

Replication of Other Phages

How well does this describe the replication of other phages? Insofar as information has become available, the pattern of synthesis of the nucleic acids and proteins seems similar. In general T2 is probably more complicated, virulent, and disruptive than most viruses; but in investigations of other viral systems, I think it is fair to say that few new features have been found. The small, single-stranded DNA phage ϕX-174 begins by making a complementary strand. From then on it proceeds as with T2, though it must depend much more on host cell functions. The single-stranded RNA phages, as f2, are so far also very small. Presumably the RNA acts directly as a messenger to specify the necessary proteins. As we have seen, ordinarily new RNA arises from the transcription of cellular or phage DNA. In the replication of f2 we know that no DNA intermediate is involved. The RNA phage seemingly induces the formation of an enzyme (or enzymes) capable of replicating RNA directly. The mechanism, whether by Watson-Crickery or direct copying, is currently hotly disputed.

Replication of Animal and Plant Viruses

In the study of animal viral replication radioactive isotopically marked precursors and specific inhibitors have been used to establish the patterns of synthesis of RNA or DNA. Since viruses or viral proteins can be injected into rabbits to yield specific antibodies, there are a number of immunological techniques for showing the production of various viral protein components. Biochemical and enzymological studies have yielded important results as have a multitude of physical methods—using the ultracentrifuge, paper chromatography, electrophoresis, and others. The considerable variation in size and structure of the viruses and in properties of the tissue culture cells makes definitive general statements difficult. All of this should not obscure the fundamental conclusion that these viruses operate in ways no different in principle from those elucidated so successfully with the phages. The essential features of the biochemistry are also strikingly parallel.

The RNA animal viruses have had the lion's share of investigation partly because of the huge support for polio research (F.D.R.), partly because the RNA viruses seem simpler, in general, from several technical points of view, and partly because the RNA of several animal viruses was shown itself to be infectious, a fact that stimulated a burst of interest. But progress has depended most importantly, as usual in research, on the ease of viral handling, cultivation, assay, purification, and on the availability of well-defined easily handled tissue culture host systems.

It must be kept constantly in mind, of course, that the host cell for animal viral replication is enormously larger (perhaps 1,000 times in volume) than a bacterial cell and much more complexly organized. The process of pinocytosis or phagocytosis deposits the virus in the cytoplasm, sometimes near the nucleus. Here it is stripped of its coat or envelope by enzymes. The localization of viral replication has been studied by various techniques. If radioactive viral precursors are used, infected cells can be exposed to a photographic emulsion and the sites of new virus formation observed as tracks from disintegrations of the isotopes, a technique known as radioautography. Actual particles can be seen in the electron microscope by fixation, sectioning, and staining of infected cells. Protein components or whole viruses can be identified by staining with fluorescent antibodies and observation in the optical microscope or with metal-marked antibody and observation in the electron microscope. The evidence at this point becomes somewhat confusing and contradictory. With influenza the preliminary steps of RNA replication occur in the cell nucleus followed by rapid transition to the cytoplasm, where the particles accumulate. Mengo and polio apparently are made wholly in the cytoplasm, adeno virus in the nucleus.

As with T2, these viruses must exhibit both heterocatalytic and autocatalytic functions. Mengo- and polio-infected cells reveal patterns of synthesis of macromolecules strikingly reminiscent of the T2 situation. The time scale is now hours, not minutes, however. With polio in HeLa cells,* the synthesis of host RNA is inhibited sharply within a few hours after infection. Mengo virus, like T2, interferes with the synthesis of new cellular messenger and then acts itself as a messenger using available cellular ribosomes for the protein synthesis. There is also evidence that "early proteins" are required for RNA replication. These are presumably various enzymes, certainly at least the RNA-primed RNA polymerase necessary before the nucleic acid can replicate. The evidence obtained with several RNA viruses shows an early inhibition of cell macromolecular synthesis. All RNA and protein made thereafter is viral. Shortly after their appearance, infectious RNA and then intact virus can be demonstrated.

Many of the DNA animal viruses are quite large and complex in

---

* HeLa is an acronym for "*H*enrietta *L*acks," a patient with a cervical cancer from which the initial cells of this designation were taken. These cells have proved beautifully adapted to culture and viral study. It seems likely that there is a greater weight of HeLa cells in the world than there ever was Henrietta Lacks.

structure, as vaccinia and other pox viruses. The tumor viruses and adenoviruses are not, in general, virulent in the sense of T2 and the RNA viruses, but involve complicated relationships with the cellular genetic material. (I shall have a little to say about this in the final chapter.) These properties are of extreme importance in the cancer problem, but are only beginning to be investigated in detail. So far as I know, the DNA of animal viruses is always double-stranded. As with T2, the DNA of vaccinia seems a single piece, in this instance of a molecular weight of some 160 million daltons, not too different from T2 at 130 million. Polyoma and papilloma, two tumor viruses, have DNA that is not only a single piece but circular in structure, as shown with the electron microscope. The biochemical general picture for several viruses of this group, such as strains of vaccinia, adenoviruses, and pseudorabies, seems quite parallel to the patterns observed with T2.

By comparison, our knowledge of the biochemistry of plant virus replication is rudimentary, mainly because we have no really suitable tissue culture systems. But with the possible exception that cell energy metabolism may be stimulated after infection, the other known details are quite parallel.

Assembly or Maturation

It is rather anticlimatic to discuss assembly of viruses because we know little about it. We can nearly sum our knowledge by saying that once the nucleic acid has been replicated and the structural protein is available, assembly begins. It also seems clear with all viruses so far investigated that these processes are somehow synchronized or regulated so that protein *is* available just at the time the first nucleic acid replicas appear. The mechanism of this regulation is, in fact, one of the most interesting aspects of virology at present, because of the implication that it may serve as a model again. In multicellular plants and animals, regulation, which governs embryological development and the entire series of events leading to cell specialization and multiplication, is a key secret. Our knowledge of bacteriophage assembly comes almost exclusively from Kellenberger's work with the electron microscope (see Figure 7·5).

That the problem of phage assembly is a real one can be understood again in terms of T2 as a rather extreme case. This virus has a DNA of a total length of some 65 microns. As the DNA replicates, in a cell about 1.5 microns in length, it produces a pool of about 20 such molecules. From this incredible can of worms must be withdrawn each single molecule of DNA, which must then be neatly folded into a phage head about 0.1 micron in diameter. Kellenberger has evidence suggesting the involvement of a proteinaceous "condensation principle." It seems almost certain that the nucleic acid folds up first and that the coat protein is applied afterward. How the protein knows where to go, how it knows where to put the elaborate tail structure, and so on, are largely a mystery. Kellenberger has recently published pictures of phages with two or more tails, located at vertices of the icosahedron. Other variants of the normal head morphology suggest that the process of assembly is not under the sort of rigid control that dictates nucleic acid replication and protein synthesis. Probably the protein subunits fit together largely because of their inherent structure, rather than because there is a direct genetic blueprint for assembly; and as with a dime store picture puzzle, there is room for misfits.

Studies of the plant viruses have contributed greatly to the problem of assembly. W. H. Takahashi showed that a protein that occurs in substantial quantities in TMV-infected plants not only is similar to the protein of the virus but is capable of assembling itself completely in vitro into rods for all the world like those of the virus. The only differences are that the protein subunits are stacked a little differently and the rods contain no nucleic acid and do not know where to stop—they come in all assorted lengths. Heinz Fraenkel-Conrat was able to carry this process even further in a really remarkable experiment. He succeeded in isolating the RNA of TMV free from protein and the protein free from nucleic acid. Neither was infectious.* Upon combining the two under correct conditions they reconstituted intact, infectious virus no different in any property from natural TMV. I shall never cease to admire Fraenkel-Conrat for trying such a radical experiment. As a chemistry professor of mine once said, about something quite different, "This is the kind of experiment you wake up in the middle of the night thinking of. You get up and try it at 3:00 A.M. If it works you are famous, if it does not you pour it down the sink, go back to bed, and don't tell anyone."

Several other plant viruses (turnip yellow mosaic) and animal viruses (adeno 5) also cause the formation in the cell of extra viral protein which can form into virus-like particles devoid of nucleic acid. From such observations we can assume that the shape of the virus can be determined primarily by the structure of the protein alone. The protein of TMV is designed to fit together in a helical rod, that of turnip yellow mosaic to fit together into an icosahedron of correct size. With adenovirus, however, the protein can form not only empty polyhedra of two sizes but also empty helices. In a series of remarkable recent experiments, R. Edgar and his collaborators have been able to demonstrate that much of the assembly of T4 can occur in vitro. Several of the steps, however, do not. This may mean possible genetic control.

The animal viruses present still further complications. Electron microscopists are accumulating evidence concerning the assembly of the larger and more elaborate viruses—for instance, the myxoviruses—

---

* In later experiments he showed that the RNA is infectious by itself, but only at a very small fraction of the efficiency of the intact or reconstituted virus.

which have a helical, folded nucleoprotein core surrounded by a more or less elaborate envelope. We know little of the sequence of events, far less of the mechanism, however. Most animal viruses eventually seem to accumulate as complete or semicomplete particles in the nucleus, nucleolus, or cytoplasm, frequently in crystalline or at least close packed arrays.

VIRAL RELEASE. The simplest method of viral release seems to be that thought of by the bacterial viruses. Along with other proteins, the virus provides the information for the synthesis of a lysozyme, specifically designed to lyse (disintegrate) the cell wall. The production of this enzyme is, normally, again synchronized with the production of virus.

Some of the animal viruses, notably polio, seem to be released also by destruction of the cell, though through as yet unknown means. With others the process seems more complex, and our knowledge is restricted to the morphological evidence discussed in Chapter 7. Influenza acquires one antigenic protein during its sojourn in the nucleus. The components for another coat are found in the cytoplasm. The outer cell surface changes in immunological character under influence of the virus. Release is accomplished by a budding, and this surface contributes the outermost viral layer. Herpes is also released by budding, but the coat it acquires is unaltered cell wall; it travels into the world disguised biochemically as its former victim. Since few viruses have been studied in detail, even further mechanisms may easily be found.

Summary

To summarize the biochemistry of the parasitism of a cell by a virus, one should divide the process into several stages: (1) The virus attaches to the host by specific bonding of low energy, typically ionic. (2) The virus or its nucleic acid is introduced into the cell by any of several mechanisms depending on the type of virus and cell. (3) If the virus has been taken in intact, it becomes uncoated. (4) Viral DNA is, or becomes, two-stranded. It is transcribed into messenger RNA's. Viral RNA acts directly. (5) These messengers institute the synthesis of proteins which derange the normal cellular nucleic acid metabolism and direct it toward the replication of viral nucleic acid. (6) DNA replicates by the Watson-Crick scheme. RNA replicates by an unknown mechanism. (7) Meanwhile other messages cause the formation of viral structural components. (8) The viral particles are assembled by largely unknown mechanisms. (9) They are released by any of a variety of processes such as cell lysis or budding.

9

The Genetics of Viruses

WE HAVE ALREADY implied that viruses have genetic properties in the sense that they are host and symptom specific. It was realized early in the game, moreover, that viruses, like bacteria, could change in character—in virulence toward a given organism, for example—and that the new properties could be retained in the stock by proper cultivation. But rather than considering these inherited alterations as selected *mutations,* the bacteriologists and virologists spoke vaguely of "adaptation." The implication was that a culture changed rather as though individual viruses exercised a sort of free will, pocketing their man-eating teeth in favor of mouse-biting teeth when it became advantageous.

With the gift of hindsight we can, I think, see several reasons for this seeming unwillingness to face biological facts. In the first place, bacteria and viruses were so little understood and so unlike higher organisms that anything seemed possible. Secondly, it was considered that mutations were quite rare events, yet with bacteria and viruses, adaptation occurs quite regularly and becomes established almost immediately. The fallacy, of course, lies in a lack of grasp of the huge number of individuals in a culture and the rapidity of the selective process in an organism with a generation time measured in minutes. In the third place, bacteria, and even more so viruses, seemed just too small to be biological enough to have genes. The famous Nobel laureate H. J. Muller had tried to determine the size of the gene of *Drosophila* (fruit flies) from x-ray data and had been able to calculate a *maximum* volume for the basic genetic element. When this turned out to be neatly the size of many viruses, some enthusiastic virologists and geneticists forgot about Muller's qualifying "maximum" and began speculating that perhaps a virus *is* a gene, somehow escaped from its natural habitat in the chromosome of some organism. As we shall see in the final chapter this idea is probably not too far from the mark except for its implication of extreme genetic simplicity. Finally, even in the 1940's it was not universally agreed that bacteria (far less viruses) had any microscopically discernible organized genetic material, far less chromosomes in any ordinary sense of the word.

Changes in these attitudes came about to no little degree because of the work with bacteriophages. It was observed that bacterial cultures that had been nearly destroyed (lysed) by phages, not infrequently produced thereafter cells resistant to the given virus. In a masterful piece of combined mathematical and virological work, Max Delbrück and S. E. Luria were able to demonstrate that these resistant bacteria are, in fact, mutants of the original culture and that they are simply *selected* and not *induced* by the virus. This brilliant paper was the first convincing demonstration with *any* organism that natural mutations are selected, not induced. Geneticists, at least, began to believe bacteria to be respectable. A few bacteriologists began to think of "adaptation" as mutation and selection.

Phage Recombination

Extending these observations, it was found that although the bacteria become phage resistant, the phages often fight back by acquiring the ability, through mutation, to attack the resistant bacteria. These *host-range* mutants of phages—for example, T2h or T4h—are easily identified by plating on a mixture of resistant and susceptible cells. The ordinary phages lyse only the original culture and give "turbid" plaques because the resistant cells overgrow them; the host-range phages lyse both cell types and give clear plaques, as shown in Figure 9·1.

Another spontaneous mutation of the phages T2 and T4 was soon noticed. Plates containing large numbers of plaques of either of these phages not infrequently show odd-looking "mottled" plaques. Occasionally a quite different plaque is found which is, in general, larger and which has a characteristic ringed appearance with a clear center and a large halo with a sharp edge (see Figure 9·1). When phages are picked from a mottled plaque they are found to consist of a mixture of the ordinary type and the ringed, haloed type. This second type came to be called "r"—for example, T2r or T4r—because it was found that in liquid culture it had the characteristic of lysing the culture more rapidly than the wild parent (T2 or T4) from which it was derived.

Both of these characteristics of phages were maintained indefinitely through repeated transfers; it was obvious that they represent mutations of the original phage. So to this extent, at least, phages now became genetically respectable; they could mutate spontaneously.

The next step was taken by Delbrück and Bailey, who infected bacteria with each of two types, T2 and T4r. These phages had different host cell characteristics and differed also with respect to the fact that the particular stock of T4 had the r characteristic. The amazing result of this simple experiment was that in addition to the production of the parental phage T2 and T4*r* there appeared two quite different types, T2*r* and T4. *The two parental phages appeard to have exchanged properties.* Pursuing this then rather incredible experiment, A. D. Hershey was able to show that phages indeed can mutate and back mutate, can be crossed, and can exchange genetic characteristics, and the exchange can be represented as though it had occurred by recombi-

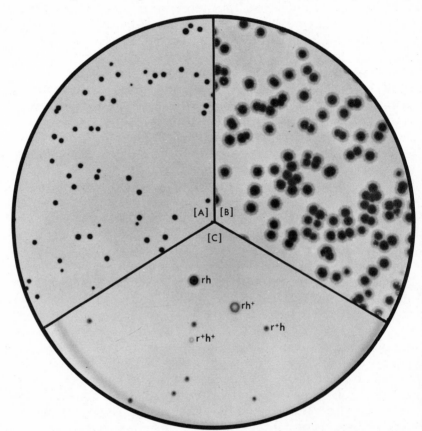

Figure 9·1. Genetic cross *r+h* × *rh+*. Each of the parental phenotypes is shown as seen by plating on a suitable strain of *E. coli* (for example, strain S). **A** is *r+h*, **B** is *rh+*. The four progeny phenotypes can be identified (as in **C**) by plating the phage obtained from the cross on a mixture of cells resistant to the wild *h+* (but susceptible to the *h* mutant) plus cells susceptible to both.

nation, in a manner formally similar to that already so well known for higher organisms.* The technique for making such a phage cross is simplicity itself. One need only infect host cells with sufficient numbers of each parental phage (usually five of each per cell) to ensure that

---

* There are important differences between recombination in phages and higher organisms, but discussion of them would lead us into considerable elaboration; suffice it to say that these complications are now almost completely understood.

virtually every cell is infected by phage of each type. The parental and progeny phenotypes are illustrated in Figure 9·1.

In previous chapters we have considered phages as models for the processes of fundamental reproduction and phenotypic expression. Through the discoveries of Delbrück, Luria, and Hershey it became apparent that we could also consider them as models for the study of the basis of recombination. Again what was good for T2 was good for the nation.

Hershey soon produced a genetic map of T2. He was able to show that the properties of host range and plaque type (both the *r* we have spoken of and another type, *m*, giving rise to minute plaques) could be exchanged in any combination. Some of the mutations seemed to be tightly clustered (pseudo alleles), others mapped as though discrete genes. The map distances seemed roughly additive, but some markers showed no apparent linkage, as though they were on separate chromosomes; in fact Hershey suggested three such linkage groups for T2, as shown in Figure 9·2. The virus began to sound for all the world like a fruit fly. How could this be? How could anything as small as T2—only

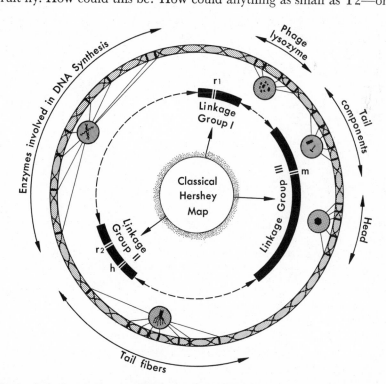

Figure 9·2. A greatly simplified sketch of the present and classical genetic maps of phage T4. Hershey's map was derived from crosses of *h* and *m* and various *r* mutants; the more complete map on which some 70 cistrons have been located comes mainly from studies of amber and temperature sensitive mutants by Edgar and Epstein.

a tenth of a micron in diameter—have mappable genes, chromosomes, mutations, back mutations, and so forth, just like a respectable organism with wings, feet, eyes, and a sex life?

The situation grew rapidly worse. Hershey and A. H. Doermann began to isolate more and more *r* stocks. With experience, *r* mutants became easy to find in any population of a few hundred T2 or T4 plaques. Soon dozens were found, but as quickly as recombination experiments could be done these mutants *all proved different,* in the sense that they could give wild-type (ordinary parental T2 or T4) recombinants when two independent isolates were crossed. If they recombined they were *genes,* by classical definition. In the course of the next decade, more and more genetic loci were defined for the T2 and T4 systems. Some of these relate to various functions, others to structural proteins. With the temperature-sensitive mutants (R. Epstein and C. Steinberg) and the amber mutants (R. Edgar) it was found that these mutations had to do with alterations anywhere in the DNA, not in a restricted locus having to do with a certain function. By their use it has proved possible to find mutant sites throughout the genome and to demonstrate not only that the entire chromosome is a single unit (not three units as believed by Hershey) but that it is genetically circular. (Every mutant can be shown to be linked to one on either side.) Our current picture of the T4 chromosome * is shown in Figure 9·2. It became obvious that something was distinctly amiss with the classical conception of the gene as the unit of heredity. This difficulty had been understood for some time by the geneticists working with other organisms, but became acute with the viruses. How on earth can a virus, as small as it is, have dozens or hundreds of genes, far less dozens or hundreds for the same property?

Molecular Genetics—The T4rII System

As usual, the paradox had its solution in the realization that we had become prisoners of our own definitions and concepts. This became apparent through a discovery by Seymour Benzer, the patron saint of molecular genetics. Although a physicist by trade, Benzer was seduced into phageology under the auspices of Delbrück. Impressed with some ideas of the geneticist Pontecorvo, he realized that what was needed to resolve the problem of the nature of the gene was a selective system with very high resolution. Benzer, in 1955, found that one cluster of *r* mutants of T4 shows an interesting property. Originally located in Hershey's second linkage group, and hence called *r*II, these mutants infect the usual host, *E. coli B,* and produce characteristic plaques (the ringed *r* plaque). But unlike ordinary T4 they fail to produce plaques on a related host, *E. coli K12 lambda.* So what? So this is one of the

---

* "Genetic circularity" does not necessarily imply mechanical circularity of the DNA; in fact it is now clear that the T4 genome is *not* a circular molecule.

more important discoveries of the modern era of biology if you are perspicacious enough to çapitalize on it. Benzer was quickly able to show that various rII mutants which yield normal numbers of plaques on *E. coli* strain B (which we shall hereafter call simply B) plate on *E. coli* strain *K12 lambda* (which we shall call K) with various efficiencies. But, in general, the efficiency on K is so low that he could detect revertants from r to normal (*wild*) or recombinants between r mutants yielding wild-type phage at extremely low levels. With some pairs the technique would have allowed him to detect a single recombinant among a million progeny particles resulting from a cross. Recollect that to do so involved only plating on B to find the total number of particles of progeny phage and also on K to find the total number of wild recombinants—a very few minutes work, with the results ready the next morning, or sooner if you are impatient. Then compare this with the situation involving such genetic subjects as *Drosophila,* where one would have actually to prepare a huge stock of flies, to perform many matings, and finally to examine under a microscope each of the million progeny flies to see whether any were recombinant, a job well calculated to drive one off his rocker.

This comparison is not intended to denigrate *Drosophila* research, which has answered many of the key questions in genetics and which still is occupied with important problems. But it is designed to show that bacterial viruses now offered answers to some questions impossible to consider with fruit flies.

What can one do with a selective system of this sort? Benzer understood that it would enable us to pursue to much finer levels important questions concerning the molecular nature of mutation and recombination, to ask the question, "What is the ultimate unit of heredity?" Workers with *Drosophila* and other higher forms had for years been showing that the gene is a complex thing, not a bead on a string. The question of how many independent r mutants could dance on the head of a pin could now be rephrased by Benzer. He could ask instead, "How big is an r marker, and how close can two r mutants be located on the chromosome of T4 and still recombine?" The rate of recombination was presumed directly related to the distance apart of the markers in question. And since we now know that the chromosome of the T-even phage consists of a double strand of DNA, we can even rephrase this question in molecular terms and ask how much DNA (how many nucleotides) must be altered to produce a mutation and how many must separate two r markers to allow them to recombine. This, then, offers an approach to the question of the ultimate nature of the informational unit in the informational molecule of nucleic acid.

THE MOLECULAR UNITS OF MUTATION AND RECOMBINATION. Benzer isolated several dozen independent r mutants by simply plating stocks of T4 on B and selecting any plaques which had the rII character. He developed ingeniously simple techniques for examining the progeny of crosses. A number of important and astonishing results followed.

Mutations did *not* occur randomly. Many appeared unique and gave demonstrable recombination with all others. But several "hot spots" were found—independent mutations occurring repeatedly apparently at the identical place, in that crossing of members of the hot spot gave no detectable recombinants. These results suggested the possibility of defining in physical or chemical terms the minimal event (*muton*) leading to a mutation. In addition, of course, the system suggested definition of a minimal structure (*recon*) capable of recombination. Although the technique would have allowed detection of recombinants at levels as low as one in 100,000,000, Benzer found none at levels below one in 10,000. A rough calculation was made based on (1) the known amount of nucleic acid in T4, (2) the known genetic map of T4, (3) the assumption that recombination is equally probable anywhere in the molecule. The result suggested that the ultimate unit of recombination and mutation was no more than a few, and perhaps a *single,* nucleotide pair of the DNA.

Benzer found that some of his *r*II mutants reverted rapidly, others seemingly never. He was able to show that these latter mutations occur as the result of deletion of a group of nucleotides of the DNA. The proof of this lay in the demonstration that markers lying just outside the presumed deletion actually recombine less readily than normal, that they are closer together because of the missing piece. The likelihood of this piece being replaced in exact sequence by mutation is, of course, virtually zero. Many of the mutations, however, occur and/or revert so frequently that it is difficult to believe that they can be the result of any process more complicated than changes in only a single nucleotide pair —a true point mutation. We shall see the hard evidence for this later. It is enough for the moment to state that although Benzer reduced the process of mutation to the molecular level, he showed only that the muton must be at least as small as the recon (one or a few nucleotides) but that the size of a spontaneous mutation can vary from that number to several hundred in a deletion mutant. Unfortunately complications have appeared. I. Tessman showed that much lower levels of recombination can be detected with special techniques; indeed, that recombinants occur at a level so low that there are vastly insufficient nucleotides in the DNA to account for them on Benzer's assumptions. These results probably demonstrate the falsity of the idea that recombination probability is equal at any point along the DNA. Thus there is also no fixed recon. This does not mean that Benzer was wrong in believing in a molecular basis for genetics, only that the situation is more complicated than was believed at first. Nonetheless it is clear that the recon and muton *can* be a single nucleotide.

THE MOLECULAR BASIS OF FUNCTION. With higher animals the molecular basis of function is usually not clearly discernible. One strain of cows produces more milk than another. Why? The genetic cause may be complex indeed. One strain of *Drosophila* has eyes colored differently from the ordinary. Here the cause may be less complex; we may be able to trace it to the production of a single chemical molecule responsible for the pigment. With human diabetics it is clear that one cause is a genetic defect leading to failure to make the protein hormone insulin. We have already seen in Chapter 8 that in general the genetic nucleic acid contains information that is transcribed, after several steps, in the form of a protein which may be structural or an enzyme. This protein may be part of a very complex sequence of interrelated reactions leading to some recognizable result—the phenotype. Is the protein, then, the basic unit of function? What is the relation of function to the gene?

THE AUTONOMY OF FUNCTIONAL UNITS. Benzer contributed some of the first and most important evidence in this area. The basis of his experiments lies in the observations that K cells infected with rII phage will not allow the virus to reproduce, as we know, but that if they are simultaneously infected with ordinary "wild-type" T4, both wild and rII progeny are obtained. Thus the rII phages must infect K successfully in the sense that they attach and inject their DNA; otherwise they could not multiply at all. The defect that prevents an rII phage from multiplying in K unaided by wild type T4 must lie in some later step of the replication process. But the interesting thing is that the missing function can be supplied by another phage. We must therefore assume that the defect is unitary and autonomous in the sense that it *does not* prevent the expression of the other functions nor replication of the phage (as manifested by its ability to multiply in cell B). The fact that the rII genetic region, which obviously controls this function, is only a small part of the total genetic map (about 1.4 per cent) suggests that this is only one of many functions of the virus. We might guess that perhaps all of the functions of the virus may be similarly unitary and autonomous; there is now every reason to believe that this is so.

Benzer also found that if K cells are infected with an rII phage selected at random (arbitrarily designated as type A), certain other rII mutants (type B) can *complement* the type A in the sense that cells infected with both will be lysed with production of progeny phages. This phenomenon is easily observed by seeding a plate with K cells infected with A and spotting other rII mutants on the incipient lawn. Complementing type B phages produce areas of lysis from which parental and, in general, recombinant phages can be isolated. The relationship is dichotomous and completely reciprocal. All members of the one class complement all members of the other; no member of a given class complements any member of the same class.

Thus the rII region could be divided into two subareas. The mutants of group A were shown by genetic mapping to be linearly arranged and those of the contiguous group B also. Experiments with other organisms had previously shown similar complementation (*cis-trans*) effects. The word *cistron* has been coined to designate such a genetic complementation unit. In the sense that it defines the unit of function, it is a more meaningful word in molecular terms than the classical *gene,* to which it is roughly equivalent genetically. Complementation has also been extensively studied with the mold *Neurospora,* with various bacteria and with other systems. We can infer that the principle is biologically universal.

THE SIZE OF THE COMPLEMENTATION UNIT. Although it has not been possible, so far, to identify the particular proteins whose lack is responsible for the *r*II block in *K12,* we believe, from a wealth of evidence with phages and many other organisms, that the most basic expression of phenotype is in proteins—that they are the biochemical unit of function. But it is also clear that a biologically active protein is generally itself made up of smaller polypeptide chains. This has been demonstrated to be the case with the antibody molecule, with hemoglobin, with insulin, to name a few of the best known instances. We believe that it is these chains that constitute the complementation units. Assuming that the same situation applies in the case of the *r*II region, we can now do some interesting arithmetic.

We have already said that the total size of the T2 or T4 DNA is well known, from a variety of different pieces of evidence, to correspond to a molecular weight of about 130 million daltons. If the molecular weight of a nucleotide residue is taken at an average of 333, the number of nucleotide *pairs* in T4 is 130,000,000/666 or about 197,000. Assuming that the rate of recombination observed in the *r*II region is typical of the whole phage genome, it can be estimated that the A cistron corresponds to 6 map units out of a total of 700—that is, 197,000 × 6/700 or some 1,700 nucleotide pairs—and the B cistron some 1,100. We may take 1,000–2,000 nucleotide pairs, then, as a rule-of-thumb number required to define a biologically specific polypeptide, thus as the unit of function. On the assumption that a triplet of nucleotide pairs codes for a single amino acid, this suggests a polypeptide chain of 300 to 600 amino acids or a molecular weight 50,000 to 100,000, a not unreasonable number. Most proteins so far studied by biochemists consist of units of molecular weight 20,000–50,000.

Mutagenesis

Mutation, as we know, is a rare but quite general biological event. How does it occur? There were a number of theories to account for both spontaneous mutations and those induced by irradiation (x-rays or ultraviolet light) or chemicals (colchicine). In essence they boil down to the idea that errors occur or are introduced in the duplication of the genetic material or in its separation into daughter cells. With the understanding of the nature of nucleic acid as the genetic material came the idea of deliberately causing errors. Some of the most fundamental experiments have been done with viruses. Radiation is lethal to viruses but only marginally mutagenic. The idea of using chemical *analogues* (compounds similar to the components of the nucleic acids) proved much more fruitful. The first attempts were with TMV, using 5-bromouracil (abbreviated BU) as one of the components of a nutrient mixture in which discs cut from infected leaves were floated. Unfortunately, because of the nature of the TMV system, as we have often commented, it was impossible to tell whether the resulting mutants were induced or merely selected as a result of the strongly lethal effects of the analogue. A number of experiments with other potential mutagens and phage-infected bacteria showed promise, but the first real break came as the result of work by Rose Litman and A. B. Pardee in 1955.

MUTATION INDUCED BY BASE ANALOGUES. Rose Litman reasoned that 5-BU probably did mutagenize TMV and that better demonstration of its effect could be realized in the phage system with its superior technical advantages. She performed an almost endless series of experiments, beginning in my own laboratory and continuing despite my strong advice and that of other virologists to quit in view of uniform failure. In conjunction, finally, with Pardee, she discovered the conditions necessary to facilitate the uptake of the analogue and to demonstrate its ability to induce enormous numbers of mutations. Whereas the normal rate of the appearance of various plaque mutants—notably *r* mutants—is an occasional plaque among many thousand, with the BU medium they found about 10 per cent of the plaques to be mutant.

We have already commented that mutations occur naturally, for unknown reasons. Was the function of the BU simply to kill normal phages, in some unknown way, and hence to select for natural mutants? Was it to increase the likelihood of these random mutations? These questions could be answered unequivocally. The rate of natural mutation is well known; it could be shown that not only the percentage of mutants among survivors but the absolute number were much greater than was accountable by selection. But a very convincing demonstration was adduced by Benzer and Ernst Freese to prove that the mechanism is quite different from natural mutation. Benzer had already shown that natural *r*II mutants appear in a certain pattern. The same proved true of the BU mutants, *but the pattern was quite different*. The inference, then, is that the mechanism of mutation is different.

What might the mechanism be? Construction of actual models of the various bases—adenine, guanine, cytosine, and thymine—showed that BU is ordinarily very much like thymine but can *occasionally* change its structure slightly to look like cytosine. The obvious inference is that perhaps the BU fools the DNA replication mechanism and is incorporated in place of thymine. In Litman and Pardee's experiment the exposure to BU had been only for a short time, yet the progeny phage kept the property indefinitely. So it cannot be that the *presence* of BU is necessary for the mutant property. Instead the BU must occasionally cause an error leading to substitution of one of the natural bases. In actuality it has been shown that BU can function in two different ways, leading to the replacement of an AT pair by a GC pair or vice versa. Such a change (Figure 9·3) is called a *transition*.

This example has been presented in some detail because it illustrates the potentialities of induced mutation and gives us insight into the actual mechanism by which deliberate alterations of the nucleic acid hereditary material can produce heritable changes. A considerable number of other examples of such changes, induced by the incorporation of surrogate nucleic acid components, soon appeared. Mutations have been induced in bacterial, animal, and plant viruses and also in the genetic material of a considerable number of higher organisms. We may, again, consider the principle of directed mutation induced by analogue incorporation as probably of universal applicability.

The most important aspect of these changes, however, is not the production of mutations, since that can be done in a variety of ways, but the fact that the biochemical nature of the change produced by analogues is usually unequivocally discernible. In other words we can say, "The introduction of a GC pair for an AT pair (a *transition*) at such-and-such a place in the T2 chromosome causes an *r* mutation with certain properties." An important point to remember, however, is that these changes are "directed" but only in a rather random way. We do *not*, as yet, have the ability to produce at will a change in a *given* AT. If you want to change your girl friend from brunette to blonde, you will still have to resort to hair dye. (Mutagens might revert her to wild type.)

MUTATIONS INDUCED BY ALTERATION OF EXISTING BASES. A quite different mechanism for inducing mutations was made available beginning in 1958 through a series of discoveries with a variety of biological objects. The above changes are made by introducing errors during reproduction. A number of biologists and biochemists had tried to produce chemical alterations in nucleic acid in its resting state. Almost simultaneously success was reported from several different laboratories. A. Loveless, in England, worked with ethyl methane sulfonate, a very active chemical well known for its ability to introduce ethyl radicals into a wide variety of organic compounds. He reasoned that perhaps the agent could penetrate the protein head of a phage and introduce ethyl groups into the actual nucleic acid with the result that errors would occur during the next cycle of infection and replication. It did. Later work showed that the reagent preferentially attacks A or G and changes them so that during the next replication the base that is inserted in the forming daughter DNA strand opposite this spot is probably chosen at random, or nearly so. In Germany, A. Gierer and K. W. Mundry showed that mutations could also be produced in the infectious RNA of TMV by nitrous acid, an agent known to have a predilection

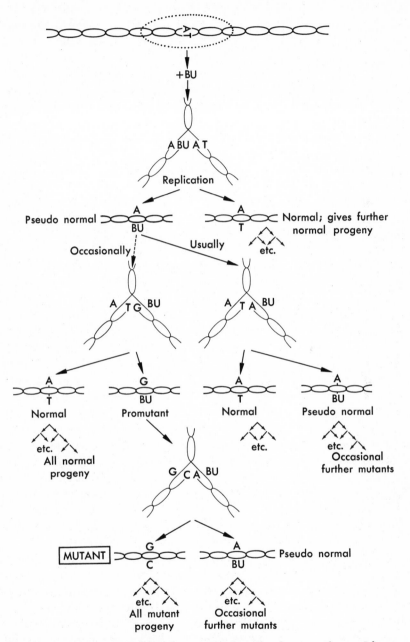

Figure 9·3. Mutation of DNA by incorporation of a base analogue 5-bromo-uracil. Note that the mutant phages *do not* contain the analogue but have undergone a transition—the replacement of an AT pair by a GC pair—because the 5-BU makes probable a wrong insertion during subsequent replications.

for attacking free amino groups. It was quickly shown by others that nitrous acid would work on the transforming principle of various bacteria and on resting bacteriophages. The exact chemical mechanism, again, is now well known. Unfortunately its action is somewhat complex. Hydroxylamine was also shown to be a very active mutagenic agent for T2, and in this instance the chemical mechanism seems quite specifically to involve the replacement, eventually, of a GC by an AT. Again, it will be noted, a so-called *transition*. Actually, in T2, the base attacked is not C but HMC (hydroxymethylcytosine) a closely related compound.

MUTAGENESIS VERSUS MOLECULAR ENVIRONMENT. Extensive use of the various mutagenic agents, largely by Freese and Benzer, evolved a new principle. Each of the agents has a typical pattern of action, producing characteristically a *few* hot spots in the rII system. The locations of these, however, differ with the particular agent used. But why should an agent affecting, for example, the HMC of T2 act differently on HMC bases located in different places in the chromosome? Why is not *every* HMC a hot spot with equal probability? One must assume that the pattern of neighboring bases plays a most important role; that a given HMC is only really susceptible if, let us say, it has thymines on each side, or if, perhaps, it is peculiarly exposed in the complexly folded DNA of a T2 head. There must be some such effect even though we do not understand it.

MUTAGENIC TRANSVERSIONS. Still another important point was made by study of the induced reversion to wild type of rII mutants. Freese found that the point mutations (changes of individual base pairs, as distinguished from deletions) caused by mutagenic agents could often be reversed. But the interesting part was that the mutations differed markedly with respect to reversal by mutagens. We have already noted that BU, for example, mutates by the process known as transition, the exchange of an AT for a GC, or vice versa. Obviously one would expect that the same, or a similar, mutagen could accomplish the reverse process. Freese found that this was indeed so. The true point mutants (those that would revert spontaneously) could be reverted with enormously greater probability by a transition mutagen. Some 30 per cent of ethyl methane sulfonate mutants however, were usually *not* reverted by transition mutagens, spontaneous mutations seldom were, and those induced by the dye proflavin were almost never reverted. Freese hypothesized that such mutants must have arisen by a process different from transition. His assumption was that originally the mutagenic process involved the replacement of an AT by a TA or by a CG. This turning upside down of a nucleotide pair he called a *transversion*. It is obvious that a transition will *not* revert a transversion. Despite a great deal of work, it is still unclear whether or not this process of transversion actually occurs. But the research did lead to another important development.

MUTAGENIC DELETIONS AND INSERTIONS. It had been known from some of Benzer's earliest work that many spontaneous mutations never revert. The usual cause of this seems to be clearly that a portion of the DNA molecule is lost in the mutagenic event. Obviously if this involves more than a very few nucleotides, the likelihood that they can be replaced just by chance in the right place and order is virtually zero. An alternative explanation to Freese's ideas of transversions was adduced by Brenner, Barnett, Crick, and Orgel. They suggested that mutations of the kind not revertable by transition mutagens might involve insertion or deletion of a nucleotide pair. L. Lerman investigated the interaction of the dye proflavin with DNA and came to the conclusion, based purely on physical measurements, that the dye indeed jams itself between adjacent base pairs. One might easily think that such an event could lead to a deletion or an insertion of an extra base at this place during DNA replication. And it is exactly with the mutants obtained from these dye mutagens that the least transition reversion was observed. This suggestion neatly explains the nonrevertibility and, in addition, raises some very exciting ideas about the relation between the DNA code and the protein derived from it.

Before we abandon the subject of mutagenesis, I should like to summarize by making explicitly the now obvious point that a mutation can indeed be a change in a single nucleotide pair but can also involve a number of more complicated alterations of the DNA.

Now Back to the Code

In the earliest speculation on the DNA-protein relationship, it was assumed that three nucleotide pairs code for a single amino acid—the so-called triplet code. Essential points to keep in mind are the following: (1) Triplets composed of combinations of 4 letters exist in 64 combinations. (2) Actually we need only 20 combinations to provide one for each of the standard amino acids. (3) This suggests that the remaining 44 combinations are either (a) *nonsensical* and code for no amino acids, or (b) *redundant* in the sense that several triplets may each stand for a single amino acid, or (c) some triplets are nonsensical, some redundant. Biochemical work with synthetic polyribonucleotides made of various combinations of bases suggested that indeed more than a single combination can code for a given amino acid and that probably nearly all of the possible triplets code for some amino acid. We can now consider, in this light, the idea of a possible insertion of a new base into the DNA code. As suggested brilliantly by Crick, Barnett, Brenner, and Watts-Tobin in a 1961 paper published in the English journal *Nature*, such a change would be catastrophic in terms of the protein produced.

As an analogy, consider the following sad folk tale, written in a triplet code in the sense that each word, which we may consider equivalent to each bit of information, is a triplet (we have introduced spaces between the words only to aid the reader; the biological triplets are continuous):

> The day was his day off but all bad for dad the big kid got the car mom hid the gin the cat ate all his lox the dog got mad and bit him his leg got big and red. . . .

Suppose we insert at random some new letter (the underlined o):

> The day was his dao yof fbu tal lba dfo rda dth ebi gki dgo tth eca rmo mhi dth egi nth eca tat eal lhi slo xth edo ggo tma dan dbi thi mhi sle ggo tbi gan dre. . . .

The result is total nonsense. If every possible three-letter word had meaning we would have, instead of the above *etaoin shrdlu,* a collection of good words, but words which would certainly not tell our story.

The idea of the English biologists, then, was to examine revertants to wild type from *r*II mutants which had been produced by means of acridine dyes, believed, as we have seen, to cause the possible loss or gain of a nucleotide pair. Such a change would make the DNA message totally different beyond the point of mutation.

A revertant from such a mutation could occur in any of several ways. With an original *deletion,* any nearby *addition* would restore to the original sense all of the message except the portion between the two mutations. This would then constitute not a true revertant, in the sense that the original damage had been rectified, but a pseudo-wild revertant or suppressor mutation, in the sense that the DNA now contains two compensating errors. Crick and his co-workers were able to show that indeed some of the apparent revertants of acridine-produced *r*II phage *are* pseudo-wild in the sense that appropriate crosses enabled them to separate the supposed wild-phage into two *r*II types and to show by mapping that the two errors had indeed occurred near each other. Thus, without knowing which is the addition or deletion they could assume that each of these mutations had produced an opposed effect, one shifting the reading frame in one direction, the other in the reverse.

We can illustrate this by deletion of a letter at random (indicated by /) in a region near the original addition to our sad tale:

> The day was his dao yof fbu tal/bad for dad the big kid got the car mom hid the gin the cat ate all his lox the dog got mad and bit him his leg got big and red. . . .

We have not really restored the message perfectly, but except for a small region between the addition and deletion it now makes good enough sense to convey the point. These findings suggest that probably all or nearly all of the triplets are code words. If any appreciable number were nonsense or "commas" or "periods," the enzyme would stop reading when one of these was produced by accident in the region between the original mutation and the suppressor. Instead of that it seems as though the enzyme can continue reading, that the protein may be damaged in this small region, but that unless this is a particularly important section the remainder of the protein can act in its correct biological role.

With this as a background they were able arbitrarily to categorize certain mutations as either plus or minus in the sense of members of the one class being able to suppress members of the other. The next step was to show that accumulation of two nearby plus mutants (or minus mutants) by an appropriate cross led to maintenance of the *r* phenotype, whereas accumulation of *three* plus or *three* minus gave again a pseudo-wild phage. *In other words the reading frame, shifted three times in the same direction, was again synchronized for most of the message leading to recovery of biological function.* Their conclusion from these findings was that indeed the code is triplet. We can see the logic by examining the effect of such changes in our folk tale. If we insert, at random, a second letter somewhere near the first (the underlined r), the message is not improved:

> The day was his dao yof fbu rta llb adf ord adt heb igk idg ott hec arm omh idt heg int hec ata tea llh isl oxt hed ogg otm ada ndb ith imh isl egg otb iga ndr. . . .

We have produced by chance four sense words, but they convey little of dad's sorrow. When we insert a third letter (the underlined z) somewhere near the other two, however, we see a miraculous change:

> The day was his dao yof fbu rta llb adz for dad the big kid got the car mom hid the gin the cat ate all his lox the dog got mad and bit him his leg got big and. . . .

The point, of course, is that only a *three-letter* code is restored to near-perfect sense by insertion (or deletion) of three random but closely located letters. A four-letter code-tale requires four insertions, and so on.

At the risk of pounding the point into the ground, I should like to note again that this most elegant confirmation of the nature of the genetic code and its reading is all based on a series of inductions built up over decades. No one has yet *seen* the nucleotide sequence of DNA (though people are working hard on just this), but we have great confidence in our knowledge of its nature and mode of function. Most of our understanding of genetics has, indeed, been based on quite indirect evidence correlated by formal induction. The chain of reasoning leading from Mendel's explanation of the inheritance of flower color after mixed breeding, to the breaking of the DNA code and explanation of its translation into phenotype, will surely stand as one of the greatest triumphs of human endeavor.

The Genetics of Animal and Plant Viruses

Compared to our knowledge of the genetics of bacteriophages, the understanding of other viruses is scanty indeed. The cloning of a bacterial virus is simplicity itself; one picks a plaque with considerable assurance that all viruses therein are descendants of a single parent. F. M. Burnet performed pioneering animal virus genetic experiments by passing influenza at terminal dilution—hopefully causing an infection by a single particle—and by picking from pocks on the CAM of embryonated eggs. The markers used included such characteristics as host range and hemagglutination pattern, far from ideal phenotypes. These methods were tedious and always subject to question.

With the development of tissue culture techniques and various mutagens, however, it became possible to find and clone mutants much more easily. Work is now progressing rapidly with a number of viruses—for example, influenza, Newcastle, and polio. Mapping has begun with several viruses, most notably rabbit pox, a relative of vaccinia. Unfortunately complications exist. One obvious difficulty lies in the enormous size of animal cells; it is much less likely that vegetative viruses will intermix than in bacteria. Flu appears to contain variable amounts of genetic material in the individual members of even a clone. Polio is so small that recombination would be rare under the best of circumstances. The net result is that the field is as yet relatively undeveloped.

Plant virus genetics has been restricted almost entirely to biochemical and biophysical studies. As usual, the lack of tissue culture techniques has ruled out successful biological work or studies of recombination, even though cloning is readily possible from leaf local lesions. Much of the pioneering work on mutagens, such as nitrous acid, was done with TMV because of the facility with which this virus can be studied biochemically and biophysically. A great deal of what we know about the actual chemistry of mutagens comes from research on mutations in TMV. Since we believe that the RNA of TMV codes for only a very few proteins, this virus offers a favorable opportunity for analysis of the relation of the code to the phenotype. The complete structure of TMV protein is known, work on the sequence of its RNA is well under way, and this area holds great promise of exciting results.

Summary

The viruses, originally considered as perhaps equivalent to single genes, have proved elegant and sophisticated models for fundamental genetic study. In essence the use of bacterial and plant viruses has contributed a lion's share of information in the study of genetics at the molecular level. We now largely understand mutation as a chemical and physical process. The basic study of recombination is progressing rapidly. One of the great triumphs has been the investigation of the relationship between the nucleic acid triplet code and its protein phenotype.

The Place of Viruses in Biology and Evolution

IN THE preceding chapters we have considered the nature of viruses with T2 and T4 as the archetypes. In point of fact, however, they represent an extreme in many respects; they are most complex ultraparasites whose every effort is bent toward subversion and destruction of the cell. In Chapter 2 it was argued that the most successful viruses are those that exist in relative harmony with the host, causing a mild or unnoticeable disease. We shall now discuss those viruses that not only seem to fail to harm the host but may, in fact, be beneficial.

Masked Viruses

Many examples of such masked viruses could be cited. Among the plant viruses, potato paracrinkle, for example, causes no symptoms in certain potato hosts, but the juice of these varieties regularly causes infections in other plants. The animal viruses have presented particularly exciting aspects of the problem of masking, because many of the best known examples, as Shope rabbit papilloma, are involved in carcinogenesis (cancer formation). Some adenoviruses can apparently be carried masked in human hosts. Herpes simplex, also, seemingly exists in an unobjectionable relationship with almost all adult humans, causing overt expression, usually as cold sores, only when aroused in some way by stress. Many insect viruses are latent, coming to light only when the host is stimulated with certain chemicals or when another variety of insect is exposed. With bacteria, the phenomenon seems most common. It has been speculated that possibly all bacteria harbor latent phages.

Other "inapparent" or "masked" or "latent" viruses have been detected by use of the microscope, the electron microscope, or immunological techniques. It is obvious that there is a whole spectrum of degrees of latency. Because of the wide range of often ill-defined effects, virologists have been unable to agree even on uniform terminology, far less concrete definitions.

Interest in the problems of masking or latency has stemmed from several sources. One is just plain curiosity, that never-failing stimulus to scientific research. A second is the possibility of latent viruses being intimately involved in the cancer problem. A third concerns the question of the evolutionary relationship of the virus and host. As has so often proved the case, bacterial viruses have provided the most easily defined and controlled (if perhaps extreme) systems.

Lysogenic Bacteria

During the middle ages of phage research (the period from 1920 to 1935) there were numerous reports of bacteria that appeared to be perfectly normal, could be isolated by standard technique again and again, but always caused lysis when introduced into a culture of some other strain of bacteria, called the *indicator* strain. Attempts, many of which were sloppily conceived or executed, were made to divest such lysogenic bacteria of their apparent content of viruses. As the modern era dawned, attention was focused on the virulent phages. A dogma was promulgated to the effect that lysogeny could probably all be explained on the basis of bad technique. Demonstration of lysogeny was, in fact, only really accepted after the careful work of E. and E. Wollman and especially after a series of experiments published in 1950 by André Lwoff (Nobel laureate, 1965) who carried *B. megaterium* through 19 generations in microdrops. At each division one daughter cell was removed with some of the liquid. The cell was used to start a culture. Every such culture was lysogenic. Each sample of fluid was plated for phage. None was ever found. Obviously by the nineteenth generation any original phage contamination had been diluted about a millionfold. These beautifully conceived and carefully executed experiments led to the conclusion that the virus must be carried in a latent, undetectable form, coming to expression as infective phage only as a rare (10^{-2} to 10^{-5}) event in a large population of such cells. The antilysogeny dogma collapsed and lysogenic bacteria became respectable, another splendid demonstration of the value of the right person doing the right experiment at the right time.

In the course of the next few years it was clearly shown that the phages from lysogenic bacteria are rather different from the large T-phages. In many instances they infect the indicator strain, reproduce, lyse it, and so on, for all the world like T2. But when they infect a suitable host under the proper conditions they can establish a new lysogenic relationship. A lysogenized cell is immune to the type of phage that lysogenizes it. Such phages are called *temperate,* to distinguish them from the T2-like *virulent* phages. Clearly the carried temperate phage must be inside the cell, and clearly it must multiply in some sort of synchrony with the cell since it was still present at the original levels after the 19 generations of Lwoff's experiment. But attempts to demonstrate the presence of the phage inside the cell failed utterly. Obviously it is carried in a noninfectious form. One might think of the vegetative form of T2. Even this, however, is an oversimplification, since it was shown by Lwoff that the *B. megaterium* phage can be aroused from its carried state into a true vegetative state by the action of ultraviolet light (or any of a variety of other agents that affect DNA). After this *induction*, the phage multiplies vegetatively in every cell, producing a hundred or so progeny per cell in a burst some 70 minutes after the UV treatment. Thus obviously it had previously been in some form other than the usual vegetative one. The name given to the temperate phage in this state of indetectable multiplication in synchrony with the cell is *prophage*. The obvious next question is the nature of the phage in this state.

Transduction

Genetic recombination in *Escherichia coli* bacteria was demonstrated by Joshua Lederberg and E. L. Tatum in 1946 (another Nobel Prize project). In an attempt to discover other examples of this fascinating process, quite akin, genetically, to sex in higher organisms, Lederberg assigned to a graduate student, Norton Zinder, the problem of finding whether *Salmonella* exhibit parallel properties. This bacterium was chosen very cleverly because it is known to exist in many variants which can be shown to be interrelated in very complicated patterns with respect to certain immunologically active components. Thus it seemed reasonable that they are able to exchange genetically determined properties. Zinder indeed found strains that are able to confer certain of their genetic properties on others. This phenomenon, quite unlike bacterial recombination, can be shown to occur even when these strains are separated by a fritted glass filter which prevents them from coming into contact. To make a long story short, Zinder was able to show that the one strain harbors a temperate virus able, rarely, to infect the second strain, establish a lysogenic relationship with it, and confer, thereby, the genetic property. This amazing process was named *transduction*. The responsible phage is called P22.

Many different properties, notably the ability to make enzymes for the production of certain amino acids or the fermentation of certain sugars, can be carried, but only very seldom is more than a single property conveyed at a time. The conclusion, since amply documented, was that the phage can carry with it a small piece of bacterial chromosome.

The Relationship of Temperate Phages to the Lysogenized Cell

Genetic investigation of various temperate phages and their ability to transduce has shown, as had been suspected, that they can be associated with the actual chromosome of the lysogenized cell. Some, as the phage *lambda* in *E. coli K12,* can attach only at a certain point and transduce only certain closely linked markers. Others (P22 in *Salmonella*) can seemingly pick up fragments from many places or perhaps anywhere on the chromosome. The exact manner of incorporation of the phage into the chromosome (or vice versa) and the mechanism by which it detaches are still not fully understood.

Clearly, however, these discoveries bring us virtually full circle. The early belief that a virus might be one of the genes of the host cell, some-how gone astray and rendered capable of separate existence, had been exploded with the demonstration of the independent biochemical and genetic complexity of such phages as T2. But now with the temperate phages it became obvious that there *is* some sort of a relationship of these masked phages with the chromosome of the host. Many phages, even some of the original T-set, are now known to be semitemperate. Some phages can be virulent under certain physiological conditions, temperate under others. Does this imply that viruses indeed arose origi-nally from cell chromosomal material with the teleological aim of aiding cells in the evolutionarily most advantageous process of genetic recom-bination? Can we assume that this is the natural sort of virus, with the virulent types representing a further evolutionary process? Or does it imply the reverse?

The Evolution of Viruses

In essence these questions lie at the heart of theories concerning the position of viruses in biology and evolution. There are two diametri-cally opposed schools of thought. The more popular one says that viruses are indeed degenerate forms of more elaborate organisms remorselessly sinking downward in the scale of evolution. The argument here is that viruses are clearly parasites, that parasitism is a well-known biological phenomenon, and that all the evidence supports the idea that parasites evolve downward. The parasite finds it less trouble to depend on other organisms for his livelihood, develops specialized methods of taking advantage of some host, and then loses function, often to the point where existence without the host becomes impossible. The parasite typically insinuates himself into a cozy environment and sucks the vital juices of the host, thus needing little biochemical, sensory, or locomotor equipment of his own. Various protozoa, flukes, roundworms, and tape-worms inhabit the gut and blood of larger forms such as mammals and fish. Lice, chiggers, amoeba, trichinae, are all too familiar to us. Hag-fish, borers, lampreys, are part of the revolting list. I find it painful to see viruses thrown into such repulsive company. They have supported me and entertained me mightily for well over a decade. In fact I am a sort of parasite on viruses. I prefer to see them cast into a nobler role. But be warned that my viewpoint is not usual. The school that I espouse says that viruses represent the evolved survivors of the first inhabitants of Earth, a noble vocation indeed. With the assurance that this argu-ment, like most such, will no doubt degenerate into questions of seman-tics and definitions, with both sides right and wrong, let us go back a few billion years to see how it all began.

It is important to note that in order to form Earth there had already been a continuous change and development from hydrogen to other elements to simple compounds to their collection into comets and planets. The astronomers now believe that given gas in space, stars will inevitably form. Given nuclear reactions, the heavier elements will be created. Planets will take shape, given appropriate conditions, and many will have a composition and environment like that of Earth. The design and pattern of this evolution have clearly been determined at each point by the makeup of the system, by the occurrence of localized, on a cosmic scale, regions of inhomogeneity. Given the same materials and conditions again, the same pattern would be observed. We may state this as evolutionary principle number one:

> *The necessary information for each hierarchical step of evolution is always contained in the properties of the components of the system.*

Does this principle apply to prebiological and biological evolution? As we shall see, there is an ever-increasing body of evidence to say that it does. While accepting responsibility for extrapolations and interpretations, let me stress that the following discussion is based on the ideas of many others. Oparin, Haldane, Ehrensvärd, Bernal, Urey, Calvin, Oró, Ponnamperuma, and Fox are among the most prominent of recent contributors of ideas, experiments, and/or calculations.

The Preorganic Earth

The components of the Earth's atmosphere, at the time of interest to us, were quite different from those of today. Like the atmosphere of the outer planets and of comets, it contained most of the atoms required for life. Carbon was present as methane (CH_4), hydrogen as the gas H_2 or as water vapor (H_2O), nitrogen as ammonia (NH_3), and sulfur as hydrogen sulfide (H_2S). The smell must have been fierce.

The landscape was not only quite different from that of today but totally devoid of life. Far less beer cans and old automobile tires, there was not even any soil, just barren rocks and minerals.

Obviously the elements of the Earth do not, by and large, exist in these forms today. Why not? The answer is that given the concentrations of the elements then existing and the localized conditions of temperature, pressure, and so forth, the above atmosphere and landscape represented the stable forms. As conditions changed, notably temperature, they evolved. Oxygen, for example, is not stable in the presence of excess hydrogen except at quite high temperatures. As the Earth cooled, these elements united to form the thermodynamically more stable water vapor. We may state this as a second evolutionary principle which provides one of the design elements of the first statement:

> *A given set of components will eventually settle into the thermodynamically stable mixture of elements and compounds.*

A key word in this statement, however, is *eventually*. Given an external source of energy, many things can happen that are *not* at the moment describable as governed by thermodynamic stability. The next stage of Earth's evolution illustrates this fact. With the cooling of the Earth, the water vapor in the atmosphere condensed as rain, filling the seas and forming lakes and rivers in a cataclysmic downpour which Ehrensvärd envisions as lasting perhaps a million years and changing the entire complexion of the Earth through erosion and mountain building. The ensuing strongly reducing atmosphere—consisting of the gases listed previously but divested of most of its water vapor—was now much more transparent to light, especially to ultraviolet light. Tremendous electrical storms, Calvin has calculated, produced intense electrical discharges. Volcanic action provided many localized regions of high temperature, perhaps to 1,000°C. As Calvin has shown in a laboratory simulation, these forms of energy and conditions would have inaugurated new chemical changes in the atmosphere and have introduced new chemical compounds into the seas. Likely components were carbon dioxide, formic acid, succinic acid, and the amino acid glycine. Even more remarkable changes have been demonstrated by Stanley Miller, working with Harold Urey (Nobel laureate, 1934). Using a mixture of methane and ammonia in an apparatus with an electrical discharge, Miller obtained a number of amino acids—for example, glycine, alanine, and aspartic acid. In extension of this work others have found that spark discharges, ultraviolet light, or thermal energy can produce an amazing array of amino acids, purines, and pyrimidines from the same autochthonous components of the prebiological Earth. The simple molecule formaldehyde has been shown capable of polymerizing into some 30 of the common sugars, with the most usual products exactly the hexoses (as glucose) and pentoses (ribose) which we know to be the aliments of life and the components of the nucleic acids. Recently Ponnamperuma has even accomplished, under primitive conditions, the synthesis of adenosine triphosphate (ATP), a precursor of nucleic acids. It provides the energy for many present-day biochemical reactions.

Why should these particular components, so fundamental to life, be formed in preference to others? This question is often considered a stickler, seeming to imply a direction or pattern to evolution. As Oró has pointed out, if we were to calculate the probability of five carbons, five nitrogens, and five hydrogens exactly falling into place to form adenine, we should consider it quite impossible. Yet given hydrogen cyanide, a simple primitive molecule, and the proper conditions, adenine is formed. Adenine was formed in evolution *not because it was "needed"* but as a consequence of the existing system. The next step occurred because adenine was available and had certain properties and so on. We see operating here in all instances the first evolutionary principle previously given, that each set of components has built into it the information for the next hierarchical step.

Another question often asked is why these compounds should have continued to exist long enough to proceed to the next step. Certainly they are not thermodynamically stable under either prebiological conditions or today's. But this is really not mysterious. The answer is that they were *kinetically* stable. This is a principle with which we are all familiar even though we may not have realized it. Gasoline, for example, exists even in an open container because an activation energy is required for its destruction. Supply this as a tiny spark, and a whole tank of gasoline can combine explosively with oxygen to yield carbon dioxide and water, the thermodynamically stable forms of the elements of gasoline under present conditions. (Please note that in the reducing atmosphere of primitive Earth, the same gasoline would have been thermodynamically stable, a spark would just have created a bit more of it.) We can, then, state a third principle of evolution:

> *Substances may exist even though they are thermodyanically unstable provided that they are kinetically stable, requiring activation energy for their destruction or transformation.*

Please note that a key factor in the destruction of organic compounds is living organisms, which did not exist at the time we are considering.

The Primordial Soup

The next step requires combination of the simple molecules. Oparin, one of the early (1930's) thinkers about these problems, envisioned the sea as the locale of these chemical events, considering it as a veritable soup of reactive building blocks. Ehrensvärd, however, calculates that the possible concentration of such molecules, on the basis of the total carbon content of the Earth and the fraction plausibly in organic form, would have been absurdly low. He assumes that evaporation along the seashore or in isolated lagoons could, over many years, form the soup in select locations. Various writers have suggested concentration of the ingredients by adsorption onto the surfaces of clays, a process that has also the attractive possibility of the clays themselves or of metallic components in them serving as catalysts. We know of many chemical reactions today catalyzed—which is to say, speeded—in this way. It is not improbable that primitive asphalts containing melanine pigments were formed. These also would be expected to show catalytic activity. We can sum up this stage by saying that there are numerous plausible ways in which the necessary chemicals for life could have been brought together into a continuous flux of reactions sparked by the intense radiation from the sun, by electrical discharges, and in appropriate places by heat from volcanic action. We have no solid knowledge of the molecules present, but experiment and calculation show that from the precursors plausibly available there would have been a strong tendency toward the formation of biologically important intermediates. Why? Not because of any design or direction or master blueprint, but just because the properties of the molecules dictated these reactions.

Abiotic Macromolecules

With the building blocks of proteins and nucleic acids probably available, we must now take a giant step between them and the macromolecules capable of autocatalytic and heterocatalytic function—the attributes of life. Most current thought implies that we shall never bridge this gap in the laboratory—I wonder how many of the same people would have made the same prediction concerning the Urey-Miller experiment. As we now know only too well from synthetic polymer chemistry, almost any di- or tri-functional simple molecule will polymerize. The possibilities for the formation of macromolecules are virtually endless, given the sort of primordial soup we have proposed. It was possible to form polyphosphates. The amino acids could have dehydrated to form random polypeptides. Sugars could have polymerized into primitive polysaccharides of a random structure. If adenosine triphosphate and other base-sugar-phosphates were available, protonucleic acids could have been made.

But why do we talk only, you may ask, of these complexes which we know to be biologically important? Nature was throwing the dice. Surely all kinds of things were made, tars, gunks, random macromolecules winding insanely about, crosslinking, branching like the hairdo of some wild, primordial Medusa half an hour after a brisk shampoo. This brings up a fourth and most familiar (though perhaps not at this level) principle:

> *For every eventually successful step, there were dozens (hundreds? millions?) of steps unsuccessful in terms of the developing world or particular niche. The unsuccessful ones vanished.*

And the situation may not have been that complicated. It seems *a priori* naïve to postulate RNA, for example, springing fully armed from the head of adenine, but we have already seen that given primitive conditions, simulated in the laboratory, we do not form a thousand amino acids of which the now familiar ones are trivial exceptions. On the contrary, glycine and alanine constituted the major products and there were few unidentified. Formaldehyde forms mainly pentoses and hexoses. Of nucleic acid bases searched for, Ponnamperuma found mainly adenine. Let me emphasize again that this implies not some supernatural direction but only the operation of our principle number one. Nature made do with the components at hand, which were not weird compounds unknown today; rather, today's biochemistry arose from the properties of the then probable intermediates. One may assume, then, that reasonably close analogues of present-day proteins and nucleic acids may well have predominated from the start.

Autocatalysis

Considering the properties of present-day macromolecules, many writers have preferred to think of proteins as the first made because of the importance of heterocatalysis. I believe firmly that the next great step must have been autocatalysis, however, for reasons that will follow, and proteins are not autocatalytic, despite the fact that biochemists in the 1940's were quite convinced they are. One could begin with DNA, but RNA seems to me the more primitive form and more attractive because it is both autocatalytic and heterocatalytic. I prefer, then, to slice through the Gordian knot with Occam's razor and arbitrarily begin with RNA.

Given primitive polysaccharides and polyphosphates as likely macromolecules, it seems to me not implausible to posit an alternating phosphate sugar chain, much like the backbone of RNA. Perhaps it had advantages of stability, perhaps the ATP present built it from the start fully equipped with a side-chain base. We know, furthermore, that synthetic RNA's of monotonous structure pair very easily into complementary duplex helices and that single-stranded RNA viruses often assume a double-stranded configuration, which may be the replicative form à la Watson-Crick in virus-infected cells. But such macromolecules, of course, give us the essentials of an autocatalyst which would change the entire situation in its niche in the primordial soup. By the processes described in Chapter 8 it would tend to reproduce itself. Even if it constituted at first only an infinitesimally small portion of the soup it would soon become predominant, since an autocatalyst, once started, increases exponentially (that is 2,4,8,16,32,64,128, . . .), limited only by the availability of components and energy.

A great deal of nonsense has been written, not too infrequently by scientists who should know better, to the effect that living structures are thermodynamically very improbable or even impossible without the assumption of some mysterious "life force." This is because living structures are ordered and hence form with loss of entropy, a process "contrary to the way things go naturally." No one is alarmed because water or minerals crystallize and lose entropy. These forms are thermodynamically stable in certain well-known environments. If an autocatalyst gains the property of self-duplication through organization at the cost of a little entropy loss, *always supplied from external sources of energy,* surely it is a cheap price. To clarify the point, let me use an analogy.

A tired, old shaggy dog story has as its punch line, "My son, life is a fountain." Well, as a matter of fact, it is. We construct fountains because we think the appearance of the water droplets and the sound of their plashing beautiful. The droplets have a completely real, if ephemeral existence. So long as we have water and pumping energy available we can keep them in constant supply. They are in a steady state and the system is thermodynamically sound because energy is continuously fed in. In other words it is a thermodynamically *open system.* One could cite innumerable other examples of materials which, like shrimp at a cocktail party, continue to exist only if they are being replaced as fast as they are destroyed. They may be inherently quite unstable in the sense of requiring little activation energy for destruction. So we now need a fifth principle of primordial evolution:

> *A substance may exist in steady-state equilibrium, even though it is by nature thermodynamically and kinetically unstable, provided it is replaced rapidly enough.*

We might call this *transitional stability.* In life, even a complicated organism exists only because it is an open system whose components are in a constant state of flux with the necessary energy externally supplied. We all have, for example, a rather substantial and constant content of ATP, yet each individual ATP molecule may last only a few milliseconds. Promptly on death the organism begins to revert toward disorganization and thermodynamic equilibrium.

With respect to evolution, the important point, of course, is that whereas previously in the history of the world we have found substances produced only by relatively random, *linear* processes, now we have a strongly directed *exponential* expansion at the expense of all available substrates and energy sources. This, to me, is the beginning of life.

Heterocatalysis

It has become apparent in recent years that nucleic acids strongly prefer to associate themselves with other structures, particularly basic proteins, counter ions (as Mg), and diamines. The ribosome, composed of RNA and protein, is in some ways the most fundamental unit of the cell, since it is here that genetic information is translated into protein phenotype. Interestingly enough the RNA of the ribosome is believed to code for its own protein. And we should not forget the RNA viruses, as TMV, which also seem to code for the duplication of the protein with which they complex their RNA. We may assume, then, that our proto-RNA in the primordial world became more stable through the accretion of amino acids. If we want to assume that things began simply and evolved, it is notable that the amino acids that have been found most common in simulated prebiological experiments are exactly those that have the most codons. Furthermore, for most of them the first two letters of the codon are identical for a given amino acid, as GCU, GCC, GCA, and GCG, for the simple amino acid alanine. This suggests that the original code was doublet, with the codon for alanine GC. We must assume, I think, that this system was too inflexible. For one thing it allows for only 16 amino acids maximum, and it seems gratuitous to assume that every one of the present amino acids happened, on the one hand, to be plentiful in the primitive world and also to fit a base pair duplex codon. Clearly a more flexible method was needed to be able to use all available amino acids for this RNA stabilization.

We know that RNA will form duplex strands. In addition to the ability to complex amino acids, then, the individual base pairs had the ability to complex with another base pair or with the end of a short nucleotide chain. If the other end of this chain could complex with the amino acid, we have proto-transfer RNA. This provided the flexibility to use any available amino acid or to change to a triplet code in this time when the protein had no function other than the stabilization of the RNA and hence could be random. The evolution of association of a given sequence of amino acids with a chain of RNA was, however, the beginning of heterocatalysis—the translation of the proto-messenger RNA code into protein.

Enzyme Formation

The great day, of course, came when by chance a protein was produced with enzymatic activity. We have already mentioned catalysts in the prebiological world in the form of clay particles and various metals. But such catalysts are often pretty nonspecific in terms of the substrate on which they will act. If a protein was created that tended to bind to such a metal and hence to stabilize itself in its existence away from the RNA it would have an advantage. When eventually such a protein had a conformation that tended to attract a particular substrate molecule to the metal and when that substrate was thereby converted into something—perhaps a nucleoside which the autocatalyst had reduced to short supply—then a revolution would occur. The autocatalysts in that niche would take a new lease on life. Now we might envision a nucleoprotein complex that could produce an enzyme—an RNase, let us say—which destroyed the free RNA molecules but against which it was protected by its association with a protein. We might also assume that a most advantageous early step would be development of an RNA polymerase, a catalyst speeding the linking together of nucleotides. Whether this particle sounds to you like a protovirus or a protoribosome begins to be a matter involving personal prejudices. Maybe we can be reasonable and charitable and say that the two developed in parallel.

And on into the Night

From here on things could grow more complicated at an exponential rate. Clearly the more functions our protovirus or protoribosome messenger could amass, the more successful genes it could hook on, the better. The more structure it could acquire, the more it could reserve its biochemical cleverness for itself instead of broadcasting its products *pro bono publico*. Somewhere along the line it must have become clear that DNA had properties of structure and stability that made it more suitable as the parent source of genetic information, existing as a more efficient autocatalytic alter ego to its companion heterocatalytic RNA. But a proto-DNA, associated with basic proteins like our proto-RNA, sounds like a protogene. Such ramifications of function would, of course, increasingly demand organization to improve the efficiency of the various specialized components. We are led, then, to the acquisition of a limiting membrane. Many find this—the creation of the living cell—a chasm impossible to leap, yet we now have two startling observations. Fox has shown that a mixture of dry amino acids in a depression in a chunk of lava will, on heating to 170°C and mixing with a salt solution, form "microspheres" which have much the size and appearance of bacterial cells. Investigation of the phospholipids that now form the well-known double membranes of all cellular structures has shown that the component molecules will spontaneously aggregate into a membrane-like structure. This can be accomplished completely in vitro with no intervention of enzymes or genetic information. These observations, then, suggest that our principle number one can account for cell formation.

And so it goes, with the development of linked biochemical pathways, the acquisition of the ability to convert sunlight directly into biochemical bond energy (photosynthesis), the specialization of cells and their assembly into ever more complex organisms.

Finally, it seems to me quite explicit in what we have seen that any planet the size of the Earth located similarly relative to a source of radiant energy would experience the same general evolution. The raw materials seem to be universally distributed and each step of the process has occurred because of the properties of the components. The more we learn, the less reason there seems to be to believe that the evolution of life came about through some one-in-a-zillion chance. As a famous old Jewish story goes, given cosmic gas clouds, the rest is *ausgerechnet* (very roughly, "obvious").

Spontaneous Generation Today

Why can we not duplicate spontaneous generation today? Perhaps we can, but in the first place we do not really know what to try to generate. We can only guess, as I have done and you can do. In the second place, we do not know for sure what substrates were necessary nor what conditions. In the third place our test-tube protoviruses would find the world today a hard place to exist in. Why? Where are the protoviruses of yesteryear? Or the protocell ribosomes or chromosomes. Like the Model T Ford and its planetary transmission, they and their components have long since been replaced by their chromed, fuel-injection, automatic-transmission, 30,000-mile-guaranteed successors. A few scientific eccentrics, like antique car addicts, mourn the happy, glorious days of yore and are interested in their history or possible re-creation. But the proto-forms themselves have gone the way of the dodo and the pterodactyl. Clearly they could not exist for any appreciable time in a world alive with more clever creatures possessed of enzymes to build, provide energy, and destroy the unwary. In their successors we can hope only to trace the faint shadow of the pioneers. Or perhaps—if we prefer mythology—like the unicorn, they never existed.

Index

Entries for viruses and phages T2 and T4 are so common that they have mostly been omitted, with listing only of the subheads. "Virus assembly," for example, is listed under "assembly."

General Editors:
> *Norman H. Giles, Yale University, Walter Kenworthy,*
> *Wheaton College, and John G. Torrey, Harvard University.*

CURRENT CONCEPTS IN BIOLOGY SERIES is designed to give the student in general biology, zoology, and botany an in-depth view of the principal aspects of life science. Each volume treats a discrete topic within the scope of general biology. Together the several volumes may be envisioned as a textbook which comes apart giving great freedom in course organization and content.

Since considerable ferment exists in the biological sciences today, it is increasingly important to keep pace with current developments. The goal of this series is to reflect that current thought for beginning students.

In essence this series is a coordinated library of books which presents to the student an understanding of current biology, its direction and content.

CURRENT CONCEPTS IN BIOLOGY SERIES

VIRUSES AND MOLECULAR BIOLOGY presents a coherent and intriguing account of the fundamental biochemistry, biophysics, and biology of all types of viruses including an assessment of their importance to man and the living world.

OTHER FORTHCOMING RELATED TITLES:

Molecular Genetics
by A. Gib DeBusk

Biology of Bacteria
by Kenneth V. Thimann

Algae and Fungi
by Harold C. Bold and C. J. Alexopoulos

Biology of Protozoa
by William Balamuth

THE MACMILLAN COMPANY, 866 Third Avenue, New York 10022

DATE DUE

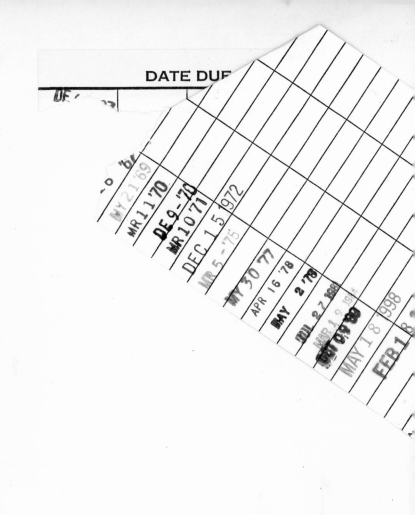